D1593802

advance praise for
the right fit

"Dr. Gross' manifesto on ergonomics is written for the R&D Manager, the marketing planner, as well as the corporate health and safety manager. He manages to address these disparate audiences effectively with an entertaining blend of historical perspective, general guidelines, insightful comments, and practical suggestions. This book is a valuable addition to the rapidly evolving field of ergonomics."

    —W.R. HARGREAVES, PH.D.
      President and CEO, Kinesis Corporation

"Ergonomics is a good fit for the utility industry. Cliff Gross was instrumental in creating awareness of the benefits of ergonomics at LILCO, and it has become a practical, low-cost tool for improving safety and employee morale. Since embarking on our program, LILCO has received numerous inquiries from other utilities."

    —THOMAS G. BARRACCA
      Research & Development, Long Island Lighting Company

"*The Right Fit,* an ergonomics revolution in the making, presents a powerful prophetic message for enlightened CEOs of companies whose consumer products touch or interact with humans. The visionary Cliff Gross points the way to implementing ultimate user-friendly ergonomic design principles into simplistic, but sophisticated technological innovations to achieve product differentiation and greater consumer market share.

"This book is for corporate executives. If they are not already believers in a corporate ergonomics philosophy for consumer product features, and for design of healthier workplaces to maximize productivity, they will certainly be converted by Gross's compelling page-turner book. Don't miss it. It's the perfect fit!"

    —GERALD P. KRUEGER, PH.D., CPE
      Principal Research Ergonomist, Star Mountain, Inc.

the power of **ergonomics**
as a competitive strategy

the
right
fit

Clifford M. Gross

PRODUCTIVITY PRESS
PORTLAND, OREGON

658.575
687r

© 1996 by Productivity Press, a division of Productivity, Inc.

All rights reserved. No part of this book may be reproduced or utilized in any form or by any means, electronic or mechanical, including photocopying, recording, or by any information storage and retrieval system, without permission in writing from the publisher. Additional copies of this book are available from the publisher. Discounts are available for multiple copies through the Sales Department (800-394-6868). Address all other inquiries to:

Productivity Press
P.O. Box 13390
Portland, OR 97213-0390
United States of America
Telephone: 503-235-0600
Telefax: 503-235-0909
E-mail: service@ppress.com

Illustration acknowledgments are listed on pages 233–237

Cover and page design by Bill Stanton
Composition by Boston Graphics, Inc.
Printed and bound by Edwards Brothers in the United States of America

Library of Congress Cataloging-in-Publication Data

Gross, Clifford M.
    The right fit: the power of ergonomics as a competitive strategy/
Clifford M. Gross.
      p. cm.
    Includes bibliographical references and index.
    ISBN 1-56327-111-7
    1. Design, Industrial. 2. New products. 3. Consumer satisfaction. 4. Total
quality management. I. Title.
TS171.G76 1996
658.5'75--dc20   96-19836
                                                CIP

01 00 99 98 97 96 10 9 8 7 6 5 4 3 2 1

IN MEMORY

OF MILDRED GROSS,

MY MOTHER,

A WOMAN OF ENDURING

KINDNESS AND FORTITUDE

University Libraries
Carnegie Mellon University
Pittsburgh PA 15213-3890

table of contents

publisher's message

Each year, poorly designed products and workplaces account for thousands of injuries and skyrocketing costs. That's why ergonomics—the human factor in product and workplace design—is fast becoming a major concern of manufacturers. Now one of the country's top experts argues that ergonomics will become the next strategic imperative for American business and the deciding factor by which companies ultimately succeed.

The Right Fit is a manifesto for corporate strategic decision makers to incorporate an ergonomic focus into the entire company, from the design of the workplace to its manufacturing processes and, of course, its final products. The competitive battle in manufacturing is no longer one of great innovative leaps but is rather a war of inches in process and product improvement. Ergonomics is one decisive way to win that war. Based on the science of human engineering, ergonomics designs products that create a transparent interface between the customer and the product.

This unique and foreword looking book addresses an audience of top managers and corporate strategic planners with a subject that up to now has been aimed almost exclusively at industrial designers and engineers. Making ergonomic quality the focus of a company's overall strategy will result in better quality products that become industry standards for excellence (best-in-class); reduced time to market; lower costs in lost productivity, workplace injuries, and product liability costs; higher customer satisfaction; and safer, more comfortable products and workplaces. Making products that fit makes good business sense. More importantly, it will give an executive or manager a new perspective and strategic tool to help their company survive, compete, and be successful in the fast changing marketplace.

Dr. Clifford M. Gross has written a brilliant nontechnical introduction to ergonomics. He is a leader and inventor in the emerging field of biomechanically based ergonomics. He founded The Biomechanics Corporation of America and established corporate ergonomic quality programs for many Fortune 500 companies. He is currently a Research Professor at the University of South Florida, College of Public Health. He is also the Director of the university's Center for Product Ergonomics, the first such center in the United States. Dr. Gross holds several patents for ergonomic products and processes.

We are grateful to Dr. Gross for choosing Productivity Press to publish his first book on ergonomics. In addition, we wish to thank all those who have participated in shaping this manuscript and bringing it to bound book: Diane Asay, editor in chief, for discovering Dr. Gross; Gary Peurasaari for editing the manuscript; Julie Zinkus for copy editing; Pauline Sullivan for proofreading; Mary Junewick for managing the production process; Boston Graphics, Inc. for typesetting and figure composition; Gordon Ekdahl of Fine Line Graphics for illustrations; and Bill Stanton, art director, for page and cover design.

Norman Bodek
Chairman

foreword

I t is an exciting opportunity to introduce you to a new technique to help bring competitive advantage to your business. In today's environment it is getting more difficult to find areas of competitive advantage. Product development teams have been working on the objectives of speed to market, quality, and cost. With quality at the heart of any new product development process, it is critical to organize these efforts around this multifaceted objective. I like to think of quality as having the two main ingredients of voice-of-the-customer and product reliability. As an advocate of Quality Function Deployment (QFD), a method for organizing and prioritizing customer needs, I have found that the quality of your product can be only as good as the customers' ability to visualize and verbalize their needs. But to outdo your competition in understanding your customers, you have to go beyond customer-articulated needs to find the unspoken areas that can delight. The good news is that these unspoken areas can provide that elusive competitive advantage, but the bad news is that these areas can be difficult to find and hard to quantify.

One of the areas that most companies overlook in product development is ergonomics: how customers interact with products. Often product teams concentrate so intensely on function that they overlook the potential benefits of fit and form. Even when teams do put effort into ergonomics, it is based on subjective criteria with no qualifiable customer evaluation. No more! *The Right Fit* describes the tools and techniques that will give you the methods to design world class ergonomic products and confirm customer satisfaction.

At Black & Decker we made ergonomics a key design objective in the development of our new line of DeWalt professional cordless power tools. We were not the first company to make power tools with better balance and handling, but by using the process described in *The Right Fit* we were able to develop a world class product and measure the improvement versus the competition before we committed tooling to the new design. Ergonomic quality eliminates a lot of the internal politics associated with whose opinion prevails about the look and feel of the product and instead places the focus on direct, measured feedback from the customer. This not only assures the product development team that it has the best-in-class design, but it also gives them the confidence to move faster for quicker delivery to the market.

Anyone who has been involved with product development for very long knows that there are a tremendous number of variables associated with designing a successful new product. There are those factors that you directly control, such as choosing a strong project leader, assembling a capable cross-functional team, ensuring executive championship and proper resources, and implementing concurrent product development with rapid prototyping, robust design tools, and manufacturing process qualification. But as I talk with peers across different industries in the new product development area, they all agree that achieving clarity in the "fuzzy front end" of new product definition is the biggest challenge. All of us have had some successes, but how do you get them consistently? How is it that the same project team that developed a moderately successful new product can turn around and develop a world class winner? The answer is in developing processes that aid your organization in putting its skills to work on those deliverables your customers value.

As Global Program Manager for the DeWalt Cordless Professional Products, I experienced the best upfront product definition I've ever seen because of our use of Ergonomic Quality and QFD. These processes strategically guided our team through the many trade-offs that are required to deliver that "right product." In our case, we had to add cost to achieve the best ergonomic comfort, and QFD told us that the customer valued the benefit. With other products the best ergonomic comfort was achieved at no additional cost. Our initial research told us we had a winner with our DeWalt professional cordless product, but the real excitement came when our customers used the first one off tooling and told us they liked the feel so much that they didn't want to put the tool down! As a result, DeWalt professional cordless products are industry leaders.

As a practical matter, you cannot follow all of the latest management trends, but I do highly recommend investigating the potential ergonomics could have for your business. The time and effort you invest in ergonomics in your new product development process will yield some of the best return on investment you have ever made.

MIKE BRENNAN
Vice President Product Development, Black & Decker Power Tools

preface

I n the spring of 1984 I placed a call to General Motors requesting to speak with the director of ergonomics. The response was a little surprising: "Would you like finance or accounting?" came the pleasant voice at the other end. It was then I first realized the nature of the task before me. Few knew what ergonomics was yet alone how it could be used as a powerful tool to win markets and attain new heights in improved product design and customer satisfaction.

My initial training was that of a scientist in the field of biomechanics—the fusion of engineering and medicine for studying the forces on and within the body. At the time the field was barely twenty-five years old. This didn't bother me much as I was twenty-three and had just completed my Ph.D. at New York University. To my benefit I had received a thorough yet condensed introduction to the field by my advisor and professor, Dr. Erwin Tichauer. Tichauer was a meticulous scholar with an unusual background. He held a doctorate in mechanical engineering in addition to being a forensic pathologist. I am indebted to him for teaching me the benefit of viewing design problems from the perspective of the body, or in his words, "the boots of the user." He was, in a sense, biomechanics incarnate. I was his last doctoral student and he retired several months prior to my graduation. To my surprise I was offered his position as the Acting Director for the Graduate Program in Ergonomics and Biomechanics.

What I didn't know, but would soon find out, was that corporations and government agencies would often call on my advisor, Dr. Tichauer, for practical assistance. They of course now found me in his place.

To meet what appeared to be an ongoing and growing need, and to better serve organizations who needed biomechanically-based ergonomics, I established a company focused on biomechanics technology. While at the company I had the opportunity to see firsthand how ergonomics could be used as a tool to transmute organizational innovation into tangible product and marketplace advantages.

Each country has its natural advantages. In the United States innovation has traditionally been the great strength of its industrial and service companies. In recent years most of these organizations have been under siege in one form or another and as a result have been looking for a strategic insight to help them formulate and execute a successful marketplace strategy. The surest path to success is to make your weaknesses irrelevant. This entails a two-step strategy. The first step is to make your strength so strong and relentless as to impair any significant competition. The second is to partner out all non-core activities with others who have developed greatness in those areas. This book focuses on step one. There is little doubt that for many of these troubled companies, Ergonomics Quality (EQ) will become both the vision and the method for cost-effectively growing their strengths and in due course, their businesses.

I am writing this first ergonomics business book as a primer for the executive and manager who need a new perspective from which to view their products and services—a perspective that can be summarized as *creating a transparent interface between customers and products.* Empowering your products to be natural extensions of your customers, leveraging the innovative talents of your associates and competitors, is a knowledge-based strategy that any size organization can use to create a strategic advantage.

acknowledgments

I've been fortunate to have had the experiences which allowed me to formulate and share my ideas concerning the use of biomechanically based ergonomics as a strategic tool. I would like to especially thank Gary Peurasaari, Diane Asay, and Carla Comarella of Productivity Press—Gary for his insightful improvements to the manuscript, Diane for her encouragement and tenacity, and Carla for her customer interviews. I would also like to thank the following companies for having the vision to embrace ergonomics and the style to bring it to fruition in their products and services:

Black & Decker	Knoll
CNA Risk Management Group	Logitech
Cooper Power Tools	Long Island LightingCompany
DuPont	Perfect Fit Industries, Inc.

Special thanks go to Robert Broucksou, Mike Brennan, Jose Carlos Banaag, Scott Star, Rick Cooley, and Tom Barracca who as champions, infused their companies products and services with ergonomic principles.

In addition, thanks are due to Dr. Gerald Krueger for his editorial comments, John Lloyd for his help with the production of several of the figures, and to Dr. Stuart Brooks and Dr. George Newkome for their assistance and steadfast support in the establishment of the Center for Product Ergonomics at the University of South Florida.

I remember the Ghanaian poet Akpaulu once remarked, "It is amazing how much I have worked for the tiny mite of knowledge which I own." In my case, even that "mite" would not have been possible without the devotion of Elissa-Beth Gross.

1

ergonomic quality: what's in it for me?

Man is the only animal capable of directed
and purposeful evolution; he makes tools.
—ALFRED RUSSEL WALLACE

Homo sapiens are makers and users of tools. Some of our earliest
tools, discovered in Hadar, Ethiopia, are referred to as choppers
and date from 1.5 to 2.6 million years ago. From the cognitive
to the mechanical, our ability to make tools helps to define us as a
species. When a powerful tool is invented, the world evolves—paper,
movable type, electricity, light bulbs, satellites, the X-ray, the nuclear
magnetic resonance imaging device (MRI), the steam engine, the diesel
engine, the jet engine, nuclear fusion, relativity, quantum physics,
statistics, democracy, even words themselves are all tools. We make tools
to cheat our animal destiny. When our vision is not perfect we want to
see well. Our thirst for seeing extends beyond close objects to distant
galaxies, using frequencies foreign to the retina.

We are toolmakers. Tools make us stronger, improve our senses,
make us smarter, extend our reach and, in general, create a vehicle that
converts human will into reality. There is no limit to the human spirit
with its ability to create and innovate. This is our lateral evolution, our
current renaissance. It is time our toolmaking became a science—
ergonomics is the science of making great tools and products.

1

EVOLUTION OF ERGONOMICS

Ergonomics is a young science that grew out of the need to better equip military personnel during World War II. It is ironic that what was developed as a tool to make fighting more efficient is now the preferred technique for preventing cumulative musculoskeletal injuries in the workplace. As an interdisciplinary science, ergonomics draws its knowledge from several tributaries (see Figure 1-1).

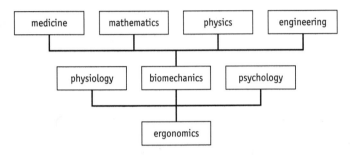

Figure 1-1. Tributaries Forming the Science of Ergonomics

The practice of ergonomics began with the collection and use of *anthropometric* data. *Anthropometry* is the science of measuring the human body to determine differences among individuals and groups. These measurements, combined with observations of how people handle tools, were used to estimate the goodness-of-fit between equipment and personnel. Early ergonomists were concerned with accommodating variously sized individuals. As performance requirements became more critical additional concerns developed: size considerations were expanded to encompass strength, reach, vision, cardiovascular capabilities, cognition, mission survivability, and most recently, cumulative musculoskeletal injury. The last of these concerns addresses the question, why ergonomics?

Ergonomics Today

In traditional manufacturing environments, safety and health concerns are separated from manufacturing and design concerns. Safety and health are addressed by personnel departments; manufacturing and design are addressed by production or research and development. This suggests one of the fundamental challenges of interdisciplinary sciences—how to address heretofore separate problems in parallel. We have learned from *biomechanically-based ergonomics* that connecting safety and engineering concerns remains a major challenge in the practice of manufacturing ergonomics. The solution is to learn and share more.

Both safety experts and industrial engineers need to become familiar with *occupational biomechanics,* the discipline that allows us to quantify forces on and within the human body while engaged in work. It is this measurement-based science that is largely responsible for the advances made in preventing cumulative musculoskeletal injury during the last decade. More to the point, occupational biomechanics is a major tool for optimizing the profitability and efficiency of manufacturing facilities, addressing both economic and safety concerns.

Using *biomechanics*, it is possible to measure the exposure of low-level, cumulative force to the body. Using biomechanical measurement tools and establishing acceptable exposure limits, such as the amount of weight that can be handled safely, it is possible to prevent musculoskeletal injuries. These measurements also provide the quantitative basis for increasing human capabilities and improving product fit.

Today, developing and engineering world class manufacturing facilities requires an unprecedented level of attention to human factors. As *product differentiation* becomes more difficult to achieve solely on technological grounds, facility and process design must now be fused into the product development cycle. This is known as building quality into the process. The common denominator in this equation is the customer. This includes everyone from the purchaser of the product to the individuals who build the products. This sensitive, pragmatic, and somewhat egalitarian view toward the use of labor has become a survival tactic for sophisticated manufacturing and service businesses. The focus on quality improvement as a competitive advantage is a logical position once we realize that well-distributed technology and capital require a new front on which to acquire a strategic advantage. Though simplistic process-driven advantages have been the mainstay of successful corporations in the 1980s and 1990s, process improvements are certain to dominate competitive agendas of every company well into the twenty-first century. Biomechanically-based ergonomics is the new process and product improvement tool that can assist companies in devising a competitive strategy for a new era. To better understand the total reach of biomechanically-based ergonomics, it is necessary to discuss its relationship to time, innovation, and *continuous improvement.*

TIME ISN'T MONEY ANYMORE

> Time goes you say? Ah no!
> Alas time stays, we go.
> —AUSTIN DOBSON, THE *PARADOX OF TIME*

In the past thirty years many critics have admonished companies for myopically focusing on short-term goals at the expense of long-term objectives. This view is highly suspect. The clear and present trend for companies is the necessity to focus on the near term to optimize products and workplaces continuously. This movement toward short-term goals is a natural outgrowth of the rapid development of knowledge and technology and its immediate application to products and services. No wonder that, despite the tradition-laden sensibilities that promise large results only in large time frames, shareholder pressures relentlessly demand and inspire management to produce results today–now.

All of this leads to the mandate of the optimal management of our most valuable resource–time. This is expressed well by Paul Levesque in his work, The *Wow Factory (1995):*

> In the past, attitudes about the value of time were considerably more relaxed than is the case today. With industrialization and the growing emphasis on productivity and efficiency came the need to promote the general awareness that wasting time was the equivalent of wasting money; the notion that "time is money" was born. Time has changed since the early days of the industrial era. Has our attitude about time kept pace with the changing times? Time is not the equivalent of money. Money is a renewable resource. It can be lost and then regained. It can be hoarded in quantity and held in reserve. Money can even be used to generate more money. Time, however, is a finite, nonrenewable resource. It passes through our fingers at a fixed rate over which we have absolutely no control. It cannot be held in reserve. And when our personal allocation runs out, as eventually it must, there's simply no more to be had. Time is much more precious than money.

As an example of this, studies by Imparato and Harari (1994) showed that a product that is six months late and on budget generates approximately one third less profit over a five-year period. Interestingly, if the product is on time and 50 percent over budget, the average profit reduction over a five-year period is only 4 percent.

The factors that are inextricably woven together with product development are product performance, product cost, development cost, and time to develop (see Figure 1-2). To achieve the needed time compression in product development it is necessary to practice a blend of ergonomics and concurrent engineering. Concurrent ergonomic engineering is discussed in greater detail in Chapter 4.

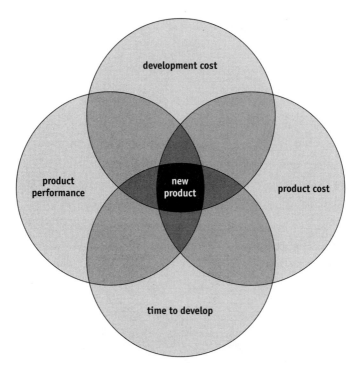

Figure 1-2. Key Factors in the Development of a New Product

The burden that today's businesses carry is the need for much shorter product and service development cycles. This burden is externally mirrored by enhanced customer expectations for improved products, as well as by the unabated demand from shareholders to provide bigger and better results in shorter periods of time. Is there a way companies can find respite from these expectations—a way to develop a clear perspective and long-term vision to keep pace with constantly shifting markets? In this time-compressed climate it is necessary for management to use common sense as well as to adapt to current events. This means that, for most enterprises, the long-term vision, if known, is best achieved with short, unequally measured steps of product and process improvement. It also means that companies must learn to innovate rapidly to survive economically. But innovation can also be used as a strategic advantage to help companies see beyond the demands of the moment, while at the same time meeting and exceeding those demands.

ERGONOMICS AND INNOVATION

God hath made man upright,
but they have sought out many inventions.
—ECCLESIASTES, VII, 29

One aspect of the added burdens placed on business activity is the rapid growth of information. To keep abreast, companies must constantly acquire more knowledge. This conscious desire and drive for businesses to use knowledge to improve products and services is directly linked to our unconscious desire for new ideas and developments. This drive manifests itself as the often referred to "necessity of invention."

The ability to tolerate randomness, ambiguity, uncertainty, and differing ideas nourishes the soil of invention. On a pragmatic level the inventive, or innovative spirit, seeks to meet current needs by providing closure between that which it knows and that which is needed. Addressing future needs with current invention develops both theory and practice. This kind of innovation is much less common and has the potential to result in the development of new sciences or schools of thought. The process of innovation requires the cross-fertilization of information, knowledge, ideas, and experience. Experience is the weakest ingredient in this mix. The ultimate goal of innovation is to understand what is and to transform it into what ought to be. From a linguistic perspective the process of innovation may be viewed as the removal of the many misunderstandings and frustrations that can arise when we use current theories and knowledge to address future needs.

Ludwig Wittgenstein aptly states this in his work, *Philosophical Investigations (1958):*

> We feel as if we had to penetrate phenomena: our investigation, however, is directed not towards phenomena, but as one might say, toward the possibilities of phenomena.... Such an investigation sheds light on our problem by clearing misunderstandings away.

Ergonomics, with its mandate to *create a transparent interface between customers and products,* is an important new process for innovation. The major points of ergonomics-based innovation are:

- Innovation is the process of transforming human will and vision into improved products and processes.

- Innovation requires the cross-fertilization of information, knowledge, ideas and experience.

- Innovation is centered around the individual but requires employees within an organization to be engaged in the innovative process.

- Innovation must be taught as a skill to those in an organization who do not think they have it.

- Innovators may be linked to form virtual work groups to achieve large-scale or widespread innovation.

Ergonomics is an important new process for innovation. However, its reliance on data about what is, and analysis of the gap between what is and what ought to be, grounds it in the scientific approach inherent in *kaizen,* or continuous improvement.

ERGONOMICS AND CONTINUOUS IMPROVEMENT

There are basic differences between ergonomics and process improvement strategies (kaizen). Programs for continuous incremental improvements have demonstrated both quality and cost advantages in the manufacturing and design process, and they deserve careful study. Kaizen focuses on the improvements in the human-process relationship rather than on the traditional technology-product relationship. The kaizen approach is an extension of the Taoist philosophy of simplicity and harmony in nature applied to pragmatic business improvement. The results have been nothing short of astonishing.

According to Imai (1986), the two approaches to industrial progress are relentless gradual effort (kaizen) and great leaps forward (innovation). As manufacturing becomes more sophisticated, differences in approach, as contrasted with differences in technology, may translate into significant differences in market penetration, product quality, and customer satisfaction. Imai's list, which compares kaizen qualities with those of innovation, clarifies the distinction (see Table 1-1).

In the past, the ability to innovate rapidly and acclimate to innovation was the great competitive strength of the United States. The heterogeneity of the U.S. population, the determination to make a better life for ourselves, the ability to tolerate ambiguity, the randomness of opportunity, and the value placed upon the individual and self-determination are some of the features that created an imperfect yet fertile ground for innovation.

Now, for U.S. companies to maintain competitiveness in the world, many quality experts advocate adopting collective, quality-based programs designed to emulate the successes the Japanese have had during the past thirty years. In Japan, however, the ascendance of automotive, electronic, and semiconductor industries has depended on strength in both kaizen methods *and* innovation. But U.S.-based companies have

Table 1-1. Kaizen vs. Innovation

QUALITIES	KAIZEN	INNOVATION
Effect	Long-term and long lasting but undramatic	Short-term but dramatic
Pace	Small steps	Big steps
Time frame	Continuous and incremental	Intermittent and non-incremental
Change	Gradual and constant	Abrupt and volatile
Involvement	Everybody	Select few champions
Approach	Collectivism, group efforts, system approach	Rugged individualism in ideas and efforts
Mode	Maintenance and improvements	Scrap and rebuild
Spark	Conventional know-how and state-of-the-art	Technological breakthroughs, new theories
Practical Requirements	Requires little investment but great effort to maintain it	Requires large investment, but little effort to maintain it
Effort Orientation	People	Technology
Evaluation Criteria	Process and efforts for better results	Results for profit
Advantage	Works well in slow growth economy	Better suited to fast growth economy

not often integrated the two approaches and may even see them as contradictory. Instead, U.S. quality and continuous improvement programs tend to be maintenance-oriented improvement strategies that only refine what currently exists. Current kaizen programs in the United States then, may not offer an approach that leverages the innovative strength of a company.

Intergrating product and process innovations. As innovation has been the past hallmark of the U.S. competitive advantage, it is necessary to find a way to cultivate the potential inventiveness of U.S. industry. Since traditionally the United States has been focused on product innovation, while kaizen, or continuous improvement focuses on process innovation, this rightly begins with a new integration of these two approaches. This integration is the basis of *applied ergonomics*. From this integrated approach a new developmental process of *continuous innovation* can evolve. Such a method would provide a structure for manifesting innovative leaps between cycles of continuous improvement, with continuous improvement being used as a tool for producing perfection between these innovative leaps (see Figures 1-3, 1-4, and 1-5).

Continuous incremental improvement works like a savings account. You open the account with the goal of saving a little bit at a time. In the first few years there is a slow steady increase in your investment. However, over time your steady incremental savings (improvements) begin to suddenly pay off in larger and larger returns (interest). The returns from innovation are far more uneven and unpredictable, and in the lean years it is continuous improvement that is doing all the work in maintaining or increasing the company's profits and market share.

From a competitive, industrial engineering perspective the manufacturing advantage to be realized is to use ergonomics as a high-technology kaizen tool. Whereas continuous improvement is limited to a group-oriented continuous improvement process, ergonomics naturally incorporates innovative leaps in product technology with

Figure 1-3. Cycle of Continuous Improvement Over Time

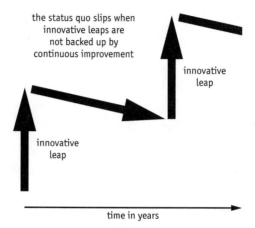

Figure 1-4. Cycle of Innovative Leaps Over Time

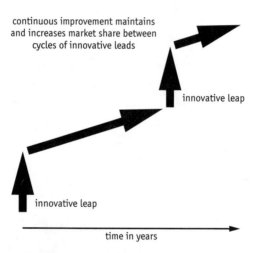

Figure 1-5. Cycle of Continuous Innovation Over Time

an interface-oriented continuous improvement process. Ergonomics is a *technology-process* tool that encompasses a complete, company-wide, *human-product* strategy throughout all aspects of design, production, and marketing.

BASIC PRINCIPLES OF ERGONOMIC QUALITY

The systematic approach to bringing biomechanically-based ergonomics into the manufacturing process is now called Ergonomic Quality (EQ). This is the next level in continuous quality improvement. It is the human factor in product and workplace design. Ergonomic quality is a high-technology improvement process that refines manufacturing systems and products through the study of how they interact with their users. EQ starts with the training of management, engineers, designers, and line employees in ergonomic techniques and responsibilities, and ends with sharing the results of implementing ergonomics with the same individuals. Between these ends EQ improves the process of manufacturing and design process and encourages continuous innovation by developing products that fit the customer. Technology is the necessary component in this approach, because interface assessments between the customer and the product require primarily quantitative, rather than intuitive, tools due to their subtlety and complexity. The technology used in these assessments is the new quantitative decision tool, biomechanics. The basic principles of EQ are straightforward:

- Technology increases the potential for user alienation and therefore increases the need for comfort.

- You need a process tool to manage technology and innovation.

- You can manage the product development process only if you can measure it.

- Create a transparent interface between your customers and your products.

- Innovation is centered around an individual, yet the success of an innovation-based system requires all team members to work in concert.

To be successful companies must continuously invest in themselves, as well as the employee, customer, and community. Only now, companies must do this more rapidly to survive. With EQ this investment usually takes four forms:

- Education concerning the human factor

- Access to physiologic and psychometric knowledge about your customers

- Development of improved tools for assessing the interface between people and products

- Experimentation with the application of ergonomic quality to refine an approach that best fits the organization's culture

New System for Creating Wealth

The old system for creating wealth was derived from three primary sources (Bralla, 1996):

1. What is taken from the ground, for example, minerals, gems, and fuels

2. What is grown in the ground, for example as grains, fruits, vegetables, fibers, and rubber

3. What is manufactured

In the new system, wealth is created from the three items above plus the delivery of services. Delivery of services adds value to the three primary sources above. The United States is the largest exporter of technology (exporting approximately $12 billion in 1990 (McRae, 1994). Interestingly, 72 percent of the U.S. gross domestic product (GDP) is obtained from services. This is the largest percentage of any country in the world. McRae estimated that by 2010 less than 10 percent of the U.S.

population will be involved in manufacturing. The vast majority of the population will be involved with adding value through services–combining services with products. In *delivery of ergonomic services,* the goal is to create a transparent interface between the consumer and the hybrid products/services (see Figure 1-6). Organizations can think of this lateral evolution of combining knowledge-based services with their products as the antidote to product and corporate extinction.

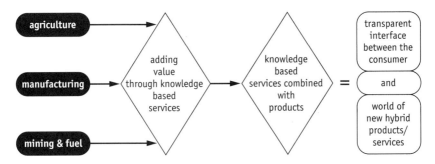

Figure 1-6. A New System of Creating Wealth by Adding Knowledge and EQ

The sheer speed of this lateral evolution necessitates group participation. A major difficulty for companies in making this transition is the misguided notion that innovation rests with a select few. To access the multiple capabilities of a company's human resources, and therefore gain the greatest leverage, individuals within an organization must innovate together. To best use the full capabilities of its human resources, a company must teach innovation as a skill to those who do not think they have it as a gift. This is definitely a bottom-up approach. But it will germinate many smaller ideas that will in turn collectively create a bouquet of successful products and safe workplaces. Today, large top-down ideas should no longer dominate an organization, but instead encourage and support an innovative-based corporate culture.

THE NEW ERGONOMIC QUALITY PARADIGM

An idealist is a person who helps
other people to be prosperous.
—HENRY FORD, 1919

Thomas Kuhn in *The Structure of Scientific Revolutions,* defined what makes science unique: scientists clearly ask and agree on the major questions. The new ergonomic quality paradigm incorporates the idea that interactions between people and products can be measured, and therefore be better understood using principles of physics, engineering, and medicine. Together, these three principles form the nexus of biomechanics. Applying them to the product/service development process reduces many of the common *prototype iterations* (replications). Ergonomics is a tool for harnessing the energy between products and their users. It takes what normally would be acceptable waste in the human-product interface and minimizes it or designs it into new improved product features and improved processes that enhance productivity.

The tools for the EQ paradigm are devices, instruments, and programs that seek to measure the human response to product use. These include:

- Human-computer-aided design software

- Measurement of muscle performance

- Measurement of forces applied to the body and their effects

- Measurement of body position and movement during
  product use

These tools are discussed in more detail in Chapter 2. Like all paradigm shifts, this one was fostered by two, unsolved problems:

1. The rapid rise in musculoskeletal injuries in a time of escalating health care costs. Musculoskeletal injuries now account for 62 percent of all workplace illnesses, or approximately 30 billion dollars annually in the United States alone.

2. The need to introduce better quality products at a faster rate due to mounting competition. Manufacturers who have implemented successful bottom-up strategies to compress and improve their product development programs have forced others to follow suit.

The new ergonomic quality paradigm is driven by the fact that all products that touch human beings are considered as extensions of the human body. By using EQ, the product's performance, fit, comfort, and productivity during use is, from the outset, improved by measuring the human-product interface.

Ergonomic Quality as a Process Model

Ergonomic quality adds a vital element to the product development process that makes the outrageous time performance demands of modern companies tenable. When designing their products, companies can now measure and use data from the interaction that occurs between the customer and the product. This is not the same thing as measuring the results of using a product or even assessing the product. Successfully addressing the human-product interface requires a broad and strong knowledge of ergonomics. In this new age of information the demand is that companies continuously fuse new knowledge into their products and workplaces at an unprecedented rate.

To be successful—to increase market share and reduce costs—companies increasingly must satisfy the customer with higher quality goods at lower cost. One way to achieve these results is to use EQ as the process tool to create a transparent interface between products and people. EQ can assist companies in rendering products that are more fully empowered as extensions of the human body, that is, better fitted to their customer. These ergonomically designed *exoskeletal products* have the potential to be so finely fitted to their users that they will greatly increase the strength, beauty, sense, cognition, and performance of the user.

Real progress and growth come when necessity and knowledge are combined in a focused, results-oriented outcome. With EQ, an improved process and an improved product are the beneficial result. Business today cannot be complacent, or merely react and adapt to the changing market. As the 1980s and 1990s have shown, this kind of company behavior leads only to reduced market share, increased injuries, and degraded productivity. Companies must act now. Market share cannot wait, product quality cannot wait, injury prevention cannot and should not wait.

WHAT YOU SHOULD KNOW

1. Time is more precious than money.

2. Ergonomics is a high-technology improvement process and biomechanics is the new quantitative decision tool. Together they create an important new process for innovation.

3. The integration of kaizen (continuous-improvement) and innovation (product-improvement) is the basis of applied ergonomics—when combined, they create a developmental process of continuous innovation.

4. Ergonomic Quality (EQ) is the systematic approach to bringing biomechanically-based ergonomics into the manufacturing process and is the next level in continuous quality improvement.

5. In the new system of wealth, knowledge-based services will dominate product offerings.

WHAT YOU SHOULD DO

1. Create a wish list of products or services you provide whose sales would benefit from enhanced ease of use.

2. Determine how your companies most precious resource—time—is spent.

3. Focus employee time on innovation and its implementation.

2

EQ, the role of the customer in product development

> If a man can write a better book, preach a better sermon,
> or make a better mouse trap than his neighbor,
> though he builds his house in the woods,
> the world will make a beaten path to his door.
> —RALPH WALDO EMERSON, 1871

Before a company commits to developing and improving their products, it needs to focus on customers. The basic principles of an ergonomic customer-centered product development strategy are as follows:

- Exceed your customer's expectations with an integrated product or service that leverages their current physical and cognitive abilities.

- Ensure that the product or service rates number one for ease of use when compared to all competitors.

- Ensure that the interface between the customer and the product is transparent, creating a new level of improved comfort and safety for the user.

EXPANDING THE DEFINITION OF THE CUSTOMER

Companies need to expand their traditional definition of the customer to encompass the evolving relationship with their employees. Traditional hierarchical reporting lines have less to do with current business needs than with comforting management with outmoded notions of controlling and marshaling human resources. Companies must be able to assemble diverse groups of people into effective work groups to achieve the goals of specific projects. Successful product development largely depends on the strength and depth of the knowledge base of the team that management brings to the development process. Often, team members have not had long-standing experience with the corporate culture. In addition, remote or tele-employees, who now number about 30 million in the United States, combined with the international character of product development teams, create more heterogeneity than ever before. Further, as knowledge is the only true hedge in the product or service development effort, it is often necessary to assemble several consulting teams to meet the demands of compressed time frames, short learning curves, and ultimate success. All of these factors point towards the need for management to tolerate ambiguity and uncertainty and to treat the members of these product-centered work groups as customers rather than employees.

The need to redefine the customer of ergonomic products, services, and workplaces becomes very apparent when ergonomic principles are applied to the manufacturing process. The very process of selecting and/or designing the manufacturing tools used to make your ergonomic products needs to be ergonomic as well. In Figure 2-1, the tool manufacturer provides ergonomic tools, *product improvement,* to its customer, the chair manufacturer. These ergonomic tools now benefit the chair manufacturer as a *process improvement* for its worker. The chair manufacturer also serves its customer by making an ergonomic chair, product improvement, that likewise, becomes *process improvement* for the user of the chair. In each case, the maker ergonomically serves the customer.

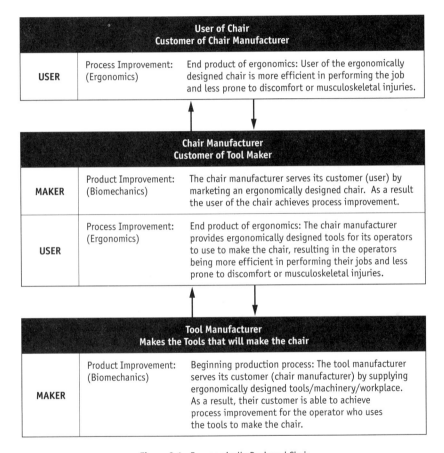

Figure 2-1. Ergonomically Designed Chair

USING ERGONOMIC BEST-IN-CLASS ANALYSIS

As Deming remarked, if we don't have a theory at the base of our actions, we are likely, through our collective efforts, to produce information rather than knowledge. For ergonomics to be successful, you must acquire knowledge about your customers' experience using products—your own products as well as those of your competitors.

The Ergonomic Plan-Do-Study-Act (PDSA) Cycle

According to Deming (1987), the traditional PDSA cycle is a strategy for acquiring knowledge for the improvement of a product or process. The elements of an ergonomic PDSA cycle are defined as follows (see Figure 2-2):

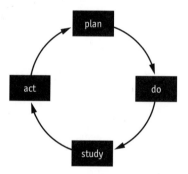

Figure 2-2. Ergonomic PDSA Cycle

Plan. Design a study to evaluate the competitive features of the interface of an ergonomically correct product or process. This is known as an *ergonomic best-in-class analysis*.

Do. Implement the ergonomic best-in-class evaluation using an appropriate experimental design.

Study. Analyze the results from a statistical and qualitative standpoint. Which product or process is best and why? What features can or should be combined in the new product? Determine if the interface between the product and the person is transparent or clumsy.

Act. Develop the product specifications based on the analysis. If necessary, repeat the process to evaluate additional features found to be lacking from the previous results.

The PDSA cycle, applied for ergonomic benefit, takes the form of an ergonomic best-in-class analysis. The simplified results from this assessment may be organized into a table for review, as in Table 2-1.

Table 2-1. Ergonomic Best-In-Class Analysis

	Product 1	Product 2	Product 3	Product 4
Biomechanical				
Pressure	7	6	5	7
Force on Joints	6	3	4	8
Muscle activity	8	5	6	9
Range-of-motion	4	4	3	6
Vibration	1	2	2	3
Comfort	7	6	4	7
Productivity	3	3	2	5
Product Performance	6	6	5	7
Ease-of Use	8	7	7	8
Average	5.55	4.66	4.22	6.66

Assess the variables on a normalized scale of 1 to 10 or the equivalent. This allows comparison of the averages among the variables. Variables are easily weighted to reflect their relative importance in the evaluation. You may think of an ergonomic best-in-class analysis, or *ergonomic assessment,* as a quantitative consumer report that gauges the quality of the interface between the customer and the product. This approach works well towards increasing the customer's acceptance and enhancing their enjoyment of the product. The goal is to make your product the best in its class. When you achieve this, repeat the process continuously to ensure that the product maintains its position of superiority (see Figure 2-3). As Alfred North Whitehead once said, "Life is an offensive, directed against the repetitious mechanism of the Universe" (1933).

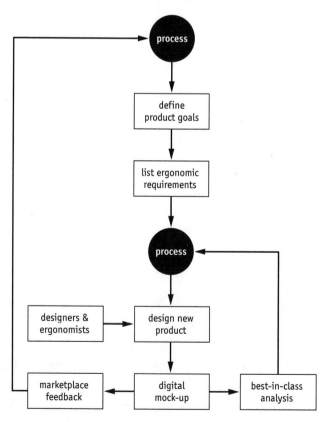

Figure 2-3. Procedure for Ergonomic Redesign of a Product

Product Design with EQ

Design all products that touch your customer with ergonomic quality in mind. The eight basic steps for ensuring EQ product design are as follows:

1. Define your customer base anthropometrically.

2. Before fabricating a product prototype, produce a digital mock-up of your product.

3. Evaluate the digital mock-up using human-computer-aided design software.

4. Ensure that the digital mock-up fits the entire proposed user base of the product.

5. Make the prototype.

6. Perform an ergonomic best-in-class analysis on the product. Include in this analysis the competitive products and your existing products that comprise the lion's share of the marketplace (75% +).

7. Incorporate those features that provide the highest ratings from the best-in-class evaluation.

8. Make a new prototype and repeat the best-in-class process.

Design of Experiments

Keki R. Bhote presents an excellent review of design of experiments in his well-regarded work *World Class Quality (1991)*. The three main practical approaches to design of experiments are traditional experimental design methods, the Taguchi method, and the Shainin techniques. Table 2-2 briefly compares these techniques. Each of these techniques

Table 2-2. Alternative Approaches to the Design of Experiments

Characteristics	Classical	Taguchi	Shainin
Principal Techniques	Fraction factorials Evolutionary optimization	Orthogonal arrays	Multiple variable component search Paired comparisons, full factorials, New product vs. Current product
Effectiveness	Good in the absence of interactions, limited optimization	Good in the absence of interactions, very limited optimization	Powerful regardless of interactions, maximum optimization
Cost/time	Moderate	Moderate if no interactions, high if interactions are present	Low
Complexity	Moderate, ANOVA and other traditional statistics required	High, S/N and ANOVA required	Low, basic math
Statistical Validity	Low	Poor	High
Versatility	Low (2 tools)	Poor (1 tool)	High (20 tools)
Scope	Used mostly in manufacturing	Can be used during design if model related input/output is known Used mostly in manufacturing	May be used at prototype, pre-production and production stages
Ease of Implementation	Moderate, good knowledge of statistics required	Poor, Knowledge of statistic combined with complexity	High, minimal statistical knowledge

has its strengths and weaknesses, and the product team needs to use prudence in their application since each project has its own specific needs.

Using the Shainin or Taguchi techniques combined with ergonomic product analysis helps us to understand and quantify the relationship between product performance and underlying biomechanical measurement. On the other hand traditional statistical modeling techniques work best for large and complex measurements. Using such techniques as *multiple regression analysis, multiple analysis of variance,* and *multiple* and *partial correlation,* you can extract the relationships between the product and its user base to improve products ergonomically. For example, *nonparametric regression* would be used to develop a systematic understanding of the relationship between ergonomic variables, such as comfort, and physiological variables, such as skin pressure. This is particularly useful for interpolating points of optimal performance (for example, comfort). By determining how physical product variables correlate with customer variables, we can better predict how customers will respond to new prototypes prior to their fabrication. In this way, the goal of creating an ergonomically superior product in the shortest period of time is more attainable. Since the ergonomic focus on product improvement requires the use of traditional statistical modeling techniques to correlate physical product variables with those of the customer, it will require that the product development team has a working knowledge of *parametric* and *nonparametric statistics.*

FITTING THE PRODUCT TO THE CUSTOMER

Most successful companies have a comprehensive strategy to market their products and services worldwide. For companies whose products physically touch customers it is imperative that they have biomechanical knowledge of their global customer's capabilities, strengths, sizes, experiences, and preferences. Table 2-3 describes the new ergonomic tools you can use to develop a quantitative, customer/product evaluation.

One Size Does Not Fit All

The first area of accommodation to be mastered in assessing your product is customer size. Often customer size may be expressed as a percentile, with the smallest sizes corresponding to the first to fifth percentiles. For example, a manufacturer of tools and vehicles needs to

Table 2-3. Some New Ergonomic Tools Used to Measure the Interface Between Customers and Products

Ergonomic Tool	Variables Measured	Benefit of Use
Human Computer Aided Design	Size accommodations, reach, vision, center-of-mass	Digital mock-up assessments reduce the time and cost for physical prototypes and increase customer/produt fit
Biomechanical Models	Joint force	Determination of the percent of customers capable of safely using products
Electromyography	Muscle electrical activity (EMG)	Sensitive measure of muscle effort among seemingly similar products
Surface Pressure Mapping	Force and/or pressure	Measure load distribution patterns between customer and product surface. Identify hot spots in the load distribution for specifically sized customers
Body Position Measurement	Location an posture of customers while using products	Helps to issue the best-in-class assessments are performed whilE customers maintain realistic product use postures
Comfort Questionnaires	Subjective assessment of perceived comfort	May be correlated with physiologic parameters to determine comfort range for particular product features

provide products that are either adjustable in size or individually sized to fit prospective users. Cooper Power Tools, for example, offers pneumatic drills in two sizes to accommodate large and small hands comfortably. To acquire a broad understanding of customer size and fit at minimum cost, the product development teams need to have access to global anthropometric databases. When these databases are incorporated into computer-based design systems, they become powerful tools for assessing digital mock-ups of products (see Figure 2-4).

Simulating Musculoskeletal Effects of Products

Human-computer-aided design is the next generation of the CAD tools that engineers and designers need to assess human-product use.

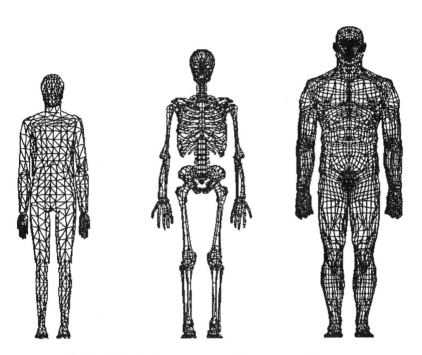

Figure 2-4. Small and Large Humanoid Used for Mock-up Evaluations

With these tools, development teams can simulate the postures and movements of customers as they use a product. The team can then evaluate the interactions between customer and product prior to fabrication of the product prototype and focus group testing. As human-computer-aided design provides a world of digital body types and sizes, these evaluations allow development teams to assess the musculoskeletal effects of the product on any size person. Product development teams could evaluate such interactions as the forces the product places on the body joints, the range of motion of the joints the product requires, the effect of the product on the customer's ability to balance, what the customer sees while using the product (with both foveal and peripheral vision), and the various size requirements of potential customers.

PRINCIPLES OF HUMAN-COMPUTER-AIDED-DESIGN

- Ensure that the product fits the entire range of potential users.

- Ensure that the requirements for product use accommodate the strength and agility of the selected user population.

- Reduce prototype iterations prior to finalizing the design specification.

- Compress the product development cycle to shorten time-to-market of improved, ergonomically correct products.

Using human-computer-aided design, it is possible, for example, to determine if a small 5th-percentile Japanese woman can operate your product as well as a large 95th-percentile U.S. or Swedish male. In the case of furniture assessments, digital mock-ups can evaluate the fit of different body types and sizes with respect to the product features. Ask questions such as: Can the smallest potential customer extend the foot rest of the recliner, and once extended, will it interfere with body joints such as the *popliteal crease* (back of knee)? All questions of this nature can be answered prior to the fabrication of the product prototype (see Figure 2-5). The successive application of these ergonomic assessments compresses the product development cycle and the cost and number of prototypes.

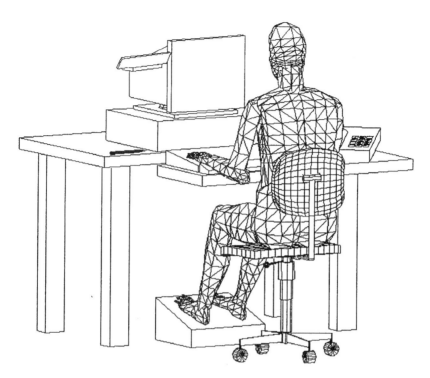

Figure 2-5. Human-Computer-Aided Figure Used To Assess Right Fit

Muscles Talk, It Pays To Listen

After you complete the customer simulation and digital mock-up, it is time to make the prototype and hold focus group testing as the next step in your ergonomic product evaluation. This next level requires additional tools; foremost among these is digital *electromyography* (EMG). This is the science of measuring a person's muscle activity during dynamic work. In ergonomics, the EMG measurement takes place while a user is testing your product. These measurements can be made for different product use scenarios.

PRINCIPLES OF EMG

- As muscles contract they produce electricity.

- The magnitude of the voltage produced is proportional to the strength of the contraction (both the force of the muscle fibers and number of fiber recruited).

- Surface electrodes may be used to conduct the current away from the body to a suitable measuring device.

- Body movement and electrode placement must be controlled to produce reliable measurements.

- Minimization of muscle activity is consistent with ease of use and is one of the goals of product design.

The basic concept with EMGs is that *muscles talk, it pays to listen* (see Figure 2-6). Muscles generate forces during contraction as a function of their cross-sectional area. Interestingly, maximum muscle strength is between 0.3-0.4 N/mm2 (Newton per millimeter squared. A Newton is the SI unit force that results in the acceleration of 1kg mass one meter per second squared). Females have approximately 70 percent of the muscle strength of males. Muscle strength peeks in our late twenties's and early thirties's and steadily declines with age (see Figure 2-7). Recording EMGs is a good technique for evaluating the function, strength, and sequencing of muscles during product use. With careful

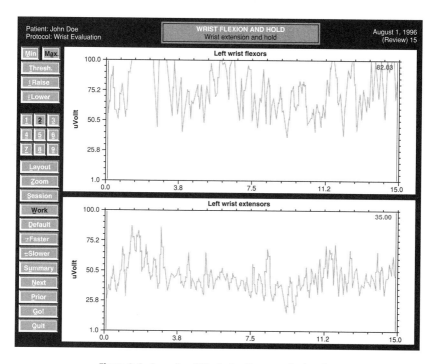

Figure 2-6. Recording EMGs During Consumer Product Use

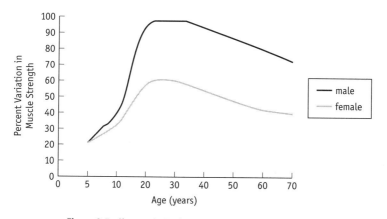

Figure 2-7. Changes in Maximum Isometric Strength with Age

technique dynamic comparisons between similar products can be reasonably accurate.

Muscles produce work. Muscles account for approximately 40 percent of the body's weight and generate the majority of forces on the body. Muscles span joints, and as they contract, they increase the load on these joints. Muscles contract in order to move or moor the body.

To use any product that comes in contact with the body requires the muscles to produce work (see Figure 2-8). In general, muscles perform either static or dynamic work. Static work appears to be an oxymoron, as true physical work requires generating a force to produce a change in distance. However, physiologic work is done even during static muscle contractions (such as holding objects), as ATP *(adenosine triphosphate)* is required to shorten or lengthen adjacent muscle fibers. During *static work* the tension of the muscle matches the external *loads* (lifting, pulling, etc.), while the length of the muscle remains nearly constant. During *dynamic work* muscles can shorten, lengthen, move at a constant velocity under maximal tension, generate a constant amount of force through lengthening and shortening, or maintain a constant contraction (for example, under electrostimulation).

Basic mechanics of muscle contraction. Most mammalian muscle contains numerous types of fiber, including fast-contracting, slow-contracting, high-endurance, and low-endurance fiber. The growth of muscles *(myogenesis)* results in a mixture of fibers within a given muscle. Nerves, to a large extent, determine muscle fiber type. Skeletal muscle fibers are cylindrical cells with diameters between 10 to 100 µm (millionths of a meter). Fiber width determines contraction strength; fiber length determines contraction velocity. Muscles produce specialized forces and, through contractions and lengthening, facilitate movement. The energy for contraction is produced by the *mitochondria* in muscle cells (see Figure 2-9). Mitochondria contain the enzymes necessary to break down *nicotinamide adenine dinucleotide phosphate* (NADH) into

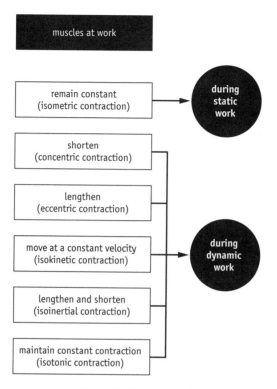

Figure 2-8. Muscles at Work

water and oxygen, forming ATP with the released chemical energy. This is a continuously occurring aerobic process.

There is an inverse relationship between the strength of a muscle contraction and the speed with which it contracts (see Figure 2-10). This may help explain why a quick shot from the hip in basketball doesn't always have the desired accuracy.

The sequence for a muscle contraction begins with a voltage in the central nervous system. The peripheral nerves then carry a current to a neuromuscular junction. At the end of the nerve, in the synaptic cleft, are small packets of the neurotransmitter called *acetylcholine* (ACh).

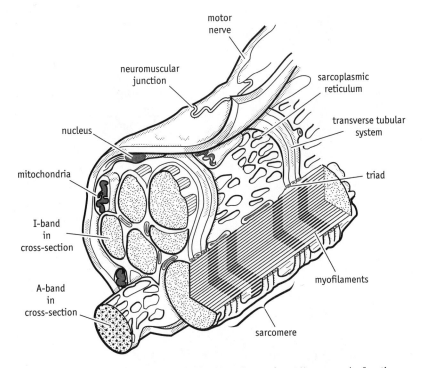

Figure 2-9. Muscle Cell Cross-section Showing Nerve Connection at Neuromuscular Junction

After the current depolarizes the ACh is released into the synaptic cleft. There it forms an electrically conducting bridge with the ACh receptor in the muscle membrane. This is the mechanism by which the voltage is produced and results in the contraction of the muscle fiber (see Figure 2-11).

Muscle activity and your product. Generally, the less muscle activity a customer requires while using your product, the better. Reduced muscle activity while using a product means less joint force, reduced metabolic cost and fatigue, and an enhanced sense of user comfort. However, not all muscle activity should be reduced below the perceptible threshold.

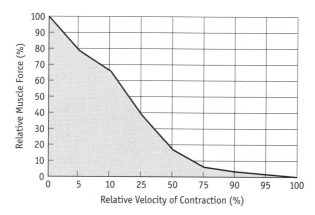

Figure 2-10. Strength of Muscle Contraction vs. Speed of Contraction

For example, the activation of an external switch requires *proprioceptive feedback* to inform the user that an activation has occurred.

Muscle fatigue is proportional to the percent of your maximum voluntary contraction (MVC), or how much effort you exert relative to your maximum effort. In general, the harder you work, the less you can work before fatigue sets in. Using a small percentage of MVC, you can work throughout the day without muscle fatigue being a limiting factor. There are, however, many exceptions to a specific cut-off score, as some muscles fatigue faster than others.

How much effort you exert relative to your maximum effort also drives your perception of comfort while you are using a product, particularly when you are using the product throughout the day (for example, hand tools, appliances, and vehicle controls). We now know that the frequency at which a muscle fires decreases with fatigue. So it appears that the body has a fantastic control system that ameliorates the effect of fatigue. During fatigue, when muscles fire at a reduced frequency, the muscles actually contract more vigorously to help prolong the production of force.

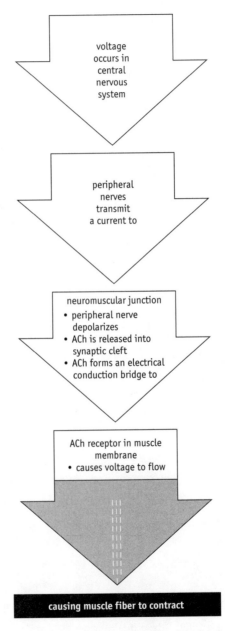

Figure 2-11. Sequence for Contraction of the Muscle

Between a Customer and Your Product

Surface pressure mapping is another useful tool for testing your product for the proper customer fit. It measures the pressure on the skin of the customer and is valuable for evaluating surfaces that come in contact with the body such as seats, beds, product grips and handles, and footwear. The technique consists of using force-sensing pressure strips placed between the product and the customer. These strips may consist of force-sensing resistors, capacitors, or thin pneumatic containers. The goal here is to measure the load distribution pattern on the skin without significantly changing the contact between the user and the product during the measurement process. Using instrumentation, the pressure information is then converted into a topographical map of the surface load pressure (see Figure 2-12). From the topographical data it is then possible to gain important objective information regarding user comfort, such as potential spots of *point loading* and *subjective correlates* of surface geometry. Point loading is a force concentrated on a small area, i.e., a point. Subjective correlates of a surface geometry are the relationships described between the pressure distribution and subject responses on comfort questionnaires.

The next step is to design these anatomically inappropriate hot spots out of the product. Generally, it is important to increase the distribution of the pressure over the largest possible useful area. These reductions in the force-per-unit area (pressure) are usually what your customer notices and feels first when testing your product in the showroom. This enhancement reduces *proprioceptive activity* (skin pressure feedback) and the time it takes to acclimate to the pressure, which provides long-term comfort to the customer. In some cases, however, specific parts of the body actually benefit from increased pressure, for example, the lumbar area of the back while sitting. It is important that companies develop and adopt a basic pressure minimization design philosophy for each of their products.

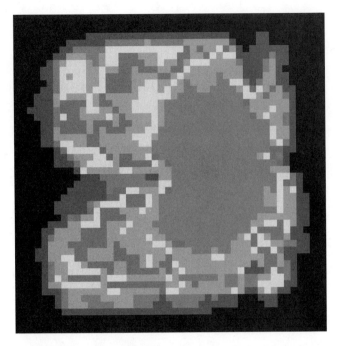

Figure 2-12. Pressure Sensing Mat and Load Distribution Information for Assessing a Seated Surface

The Body In Motion

To fully empower the product development team and help them to faithfully replicate the ergonomic best-in-class analysis under conditions similar to actual product use, it is important to measure body posture and position while your customers are using your products. Numerous systems exist for tracking the human body in motion. These systems range from easy-to-use, though not very accurate, video recordings to sophisticated, 3-D, electromagnetic tracking systems of the whole body (see Figure 2-13). With these systems you can record, digitize, and review information on three-dimensional body position to determine actual postures maintained during the use of your product. Then you need to compile frequency distributions of these postures to select the most frequently occurring body positions and movements. These postures form the basis for the physical testing of the products during the best-in-class analysis.

If You Don't Ask ...

Comfort questionnaires inquire about what the customer perceives while handling products. Whenever possible incorporate scales, such as *Likert Scales,* on the questionnaires so participants can numerically rate and combine responses about their perceptions. After compiling this data it is possible to identify the optimal product/comfort feature.

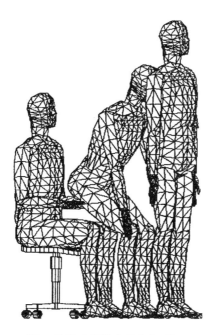

Figure 2-13. 3-D Whole Body Tracking

Educating the Customer

Once a company commits to producing EQ products, it is important to educate customers about the new ergonomic advantages of your products. This may take many different marketing forms, such as labels, identifiable markings, and publication of competitive comparisons. The point is, once your products are ergonomically superior, your customer needs to be made aware of it. This raises the bar for your competitors, and of course, necessitates repeating the best-in-class cycle yourself.

Comfort is the Key

The key to ergonomically designed products is to ensure that your customers are comfortable using your products. While comfort may seem like an ephemeral quality, it is fundamental to creating a transparent interface. Functionality combined with comfort creates customer delight. Once you capture the comfort of your customers, they will purchase your products and services.

The information gathered from these ergonomic tools, including human-computer-aided design, biomechanical models, electromyography, surface pressure mapping, body position measurement, and comfort questionnaires, is much more useful if it is acquired using a structured experimental design similar to the Taguchi or Shainin techniques. Also, it is important that your team have access to the latest biomechanical tools and expertise. One way to do this is to partner with an ergonomics consultant, company, or university, such as the Center for Product Ergonomics at the University of South Florida (see appendix).

WHAT YOU SHOULD KNOW

1. Ergonomic Quality (EQ) requires you to expand the definition of your customer to include employees.

2. The very process of selecting and/or designing the manufacturing tools used to make your ergonomic products should be ergonomic as well.

3. You may think of an ergonomic best-in-class analysis as a quantitative consumer report that gauges the quality of the interface between the customer and the product.

4. For companies whose products physically touch customers it is imperative that they have biomechanical knowledge of their customer's capabilities, strengths, sizes, experiences, and preferences.

5. Assessing product comfort requires familiarity with and access to specialized biomechanical tools, such as human-computer-aided design, elecromyography (EMG), surface pressure mapping, body-tracking equipment, and biomechanical models.

WHAT YOU SHOULD DO

1. Write a product development mission statement that incorporates ergonomic development and improvement.

2. Establish an ergonomics task force to fuse ergonomics to current product development, manufacturing, and marketing efforts.

3. Find out from marketing which products could most use ergonomics, product differentiation, and improvement. Select one product or service for fast-track ergonomic improvement.

4. Familiarize the product development and marketing teams with best-in-class assessments. Use ergonomics best-in-class analysis to objectively analyze your products or services.

5. Develop a comfort model that defines the relationship between all your product features and customer comfort.

3

ergonomic product design
and development

The real act of discovery consists
not in finding new lands but
in seeing with new eyes.

—MARCEL PROUST

The ergonomic product development process is similar to the traditional product development process as described by Ulrich and
Eppinger (1995) with one major difference: Ergonomic product
development is user-centered cognitively and physiologically (see Figure
3-1). It is an interface-oriented product development that leads to the
creation and marketing of what we call *ergonomic push products.*

ERGONOMIC PRODUCT CONCEPT DEVELOPMENT

The opportunity now exists for companies to gain significant market
share by ensuring that all of its products are ergonomically best-in-
class—a differentiation strategy based on optimizing user comfort and
product fit. Rather than pursuing a technology-only advantage, ergonomics push products offer a low-cost strategy for defining market
leadership in product categories. Ergonomic product concept development
is the cornerstone for building marketplace dominance. As Figure 3-2
demonstrates, ergonomic product concept development requires invent-

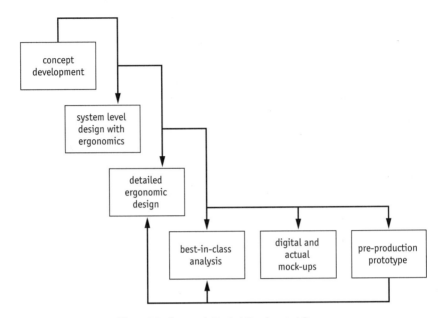

Figure 3-1. Ergonomic Product Development Process

ing new transparent interfaces for your existing product categories and in so doing, naturally extending human capacity. This new ergonomic development process goes a long way toward identifying real interface growth, improvement, and superiority in your products. It is also a process that thrives in and encourages a creative environment where ambiguity and uncertainty are tolerated.

The difference between a good human-product interface and a great one is often a war of *nanometers* or *nanoseconds*. The competitive battle in manufacturing is a war fought on two fronts, that of dramatic and sudden innovative leaps combined with a war of inch-by-inch in improvement in process and product development. Ford's Taurus is a case in point. Its innovative aerodynamic styling, combined with good interior ergonomics at an affordable price, was revolutionary and contributed to a decade of success. The evolution in product quality and

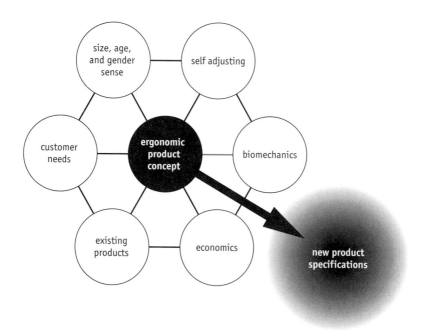

Figure 3-2. Ergonomic Product Concept Development Process

interior ergonomics that has occurred since its introduction, enables the Taurus to maintain a commanding lead in the midpriced sedan segment.

DESIGN FOR ERGONOMIC MANUFACTURABILITY

To make this new ergonomic product development process more tenable, it pays well to ask the question: What, in the best of all possible worlds, do you want? The answer to this question is invariably an exercise in opposites. I want it light, but strong; adjustable, but easy to use; inexpensive, but durable; powerful, yet compact, etc. From the concept of your product to its development, the ultimate answer is a compromise of many features and values. However, comfort should never be compromised. Comfort is the platform on which market share is won or lost. *You may have to stretch three days rations over five, but a sharp sword is a sharp sword*. Keep comfort at the top of the product feature selection hierarchy (see Figure 3-3).

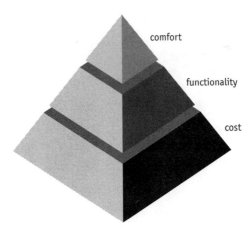

comfort

functionality

cost

Figure 3-3. Product Feature Selection Hierarchy

Perform a Needs Assessment

In Chapter 2, we discussed the importance of becoming customer-centered before developing and improving products. We also presented some of the new ergonomic tools that are available for developing a quantitative, customer/product evaluation. Another aspect of this ongoing evaluation during ergonomic product development is the needs assessment for evaluating customer needs. It is important to perform a needs assessment with individuals who are experienced with your product or your competitors' products. You can assess customer needs efficiently and quickly as follows:

1. Videotape customers using the current product and the best available competitors' products. Analyze these videos to

determine frequency of posture specific activities, for example, operating the switch, placing on a work bench, pouring detergent and so on.

1a. Alternatively, if you have the technology, electromagnetically track the customers during product use. This is more accurate than video and greatly speeds up the post-data collection analysis. The 3-D body tracking could then be read directly into a human-computer-aided design system.

2. Reconstruct the product-use scenario in the laboratory with a representative sample of your customer population. Test products according to the frequency distribution determined above. During these trials monitor body posture, joint force, muscle activity, etc., as needed to quantify the forces the product places upon the body.

3. Administer questionnaires to subjects to rate their musculoskeletal comfort and/or discomfort.

4. Determine the relationship between recorded comfort during product use and objective physical variables, for example, pressure.

5. Construct digital prototypes of the product using comfort and physical variable guidelines.

6. Add these prototypes to the baseline best-in-class analysis.

7. Refine the prototypes until your product is best-in-class.

8. Repeat as often as necessary.

Create the Ergonomic Product Aesthetic

Following the needs assessment, it will be very clear from the best-in-class assessment where your product needs improvement. Once you know the relationship between comfort and the physical parameters of your product, it is then possible to predict, within a narrow range, what categorical changes are necessary to improve your product's comfort. At this point in the process, the river of possibilities and difficulties widens and your development team needs to make imaginative and technological leaps to cross the chasm. The good news is that, for the first time, the problems with your product are precisely defined. In a sense, this is the beginning of the creative part of normal science or the normal part of applied ergonomics.

To cross this chasm in a measured manner and to create ergonomic product uniqueness requires some guidance and more than a modicum of talent. During the creative process, biomechanically-based ergonomics must migrate beyond objective product functionality to become a product aesthetic. For this purpose, it is useful to consider Dr. H. Gruber's partial list of attributes for the aesthetic experience of a contemplative object (see Figure 3-4).

These attributes, or virtues, are starting points for harnessing leaps of creativity under the ergonomic mandate of creating a transparent product interface. Sometimes, all that is required to achieve this is the fusion of existing technology in a new package. Such was the case with the lightweight, handheld grinders Cooper Power Tools developed to minimize wrist deviation and vibration transmission to the hands and fingers using a soft touch, contoured, polymeric housing.

Design for Customer Delight

Consumer value, as well as the ultimate success of a company's product, rely on the quality of the features available to the customer in the product's

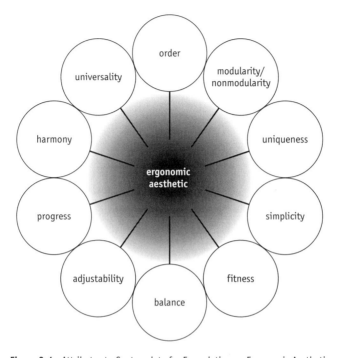

Figure 3-4. Attributes to Contemplate for Formulating an Ergonomic Aesthetic

price range. The corporate value of a specific product is the increased value of the brand name as well as the enhancement or detraction from the related corporate name. The creation of high value, low-cost ergonomic products requires the fusion of manufacturing, design, marketing, and accounting expertise (see Figure 3-5). Cost reduction is an important and common theme throughout the creation of an ergonomic product but it is not the plot. The big story in ergonomic product development is creating a transparent interface, a high value, low-cost stategy that extends from customer service to product use, both in consumer settings and in the workplace.

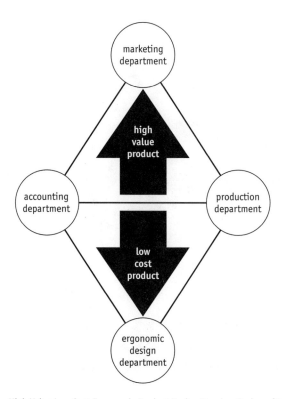

Figure 3-5. High Value Low Cost Ergonomic Product Design Requires Fusion of Departments

Consumers are feature- and price-conscious and their tolerance for uncomfortable or poorly performing products is at an all time low. Consider the unlikely event of purchasing a television without a remote control. Tolerance for poor performance further erodes as the consumer population ages, due to a lifelong experience with an increasing diversity of products. The message is clear—marketplace dominance requires the repeated creation of customer delight.

A restrictive element in the feature/price equation is how to minimize innovation costs within the shortest possible time frame. A large part of the strategic value of innovation is that it is time and cost dependent, which requires leadership in ergonomic product development to find ways of producing innovation at the lowest cost, in the shortest possible time (see Figure 3-6).

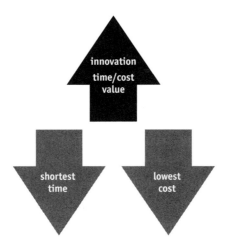

Figure 3-6. Time/Cost Basis of Innovation

Encourage Continuous Innovation

How can companies encourage continuous innovation—the development process that combines product innovation and process innovation? This brings us back to the main asset of innovation-dependent companies: knowledge workers. Dr. Drucker's remarks *(The New Realities, 1989)* drive home the importance of this new class of innovators to the success of the modern corporation:

> One of Karl Marx's insights was that capital has mobility. In this it differs from all other factors of production such as land and labor. Capital can go where it is paid the most. Knowledge now has become the real capital of a developed economy. Knowledge workers know that their knowledge, even if not very advanced, gives them freedom to move .... Everyone's knowledge has a multitude of applications.

Types of innovation. Barker *(Paradigms, 1992)* describes two major types of innovation: paradigm-enhancing and paradigm-shifting. Paradigm-enhancing innovations are major improvements on existing ideas. Paradigm-shifting is the result of a powerful new idea. It is the fundamental type of innovation and is responsible for major changes in process. This type of shift is often misunderstood or not initially accepted. It is exemplified by the inventor who believes the time has come for a new idea. The skill required for translating new and powerful ideas into products and services needs to be constantly harnessed and nourished.

A good example of a paradigm-shifting innovation is the story of Percy Le Baron Spencer, an engineer at Raytheon in 1945 (Messadie, 1991). While working on radar with wavelengths of 25 to 120 mm, Percy noticed that a piece of chocolate had melted in his pocket. His training in physics allowed him to see what had happened: The microwaves induced molecular vibration, which in turn generated heat and melted the candy. The Radar Range® was born. In 1967, Amana, a subsidiary of Raytheon, introduced the microwave oven to the home market. This paradigm shift required Raytheon to have the vision to ask and see what business they were in. In 1945, the only thing Raytheon was cooking up were military radar stations. But, in fact, the real business they were in was the vibration of molecules at the microwave wavelength, whose applications ranged from detecting enemy aircraft to rapidly cooking frozen pizza.

It is clear that after the hectic years of the 1980s and early 1990s, when many corporations scrambled to regain market share, or just to survive, a major paradigm shift occurred in the way we develop products. Ergonomic quality, because it integrates process and product improvement, is increasingly driving this paradigm shift. It supports the more modest, but equally important, paradigm-enhancing innovations as well.

For paradigm-shifting and paradigm-enhancing innovations to flourish in a corporate environment the following features are needed:

- Enriched availability and flow of information

- High toleration of ambiguity

- Reward for innovation

Enriched availability and flow occurs when information is allowed to flow seamlessly through an organization. A very important aspect of the successful flow of information is the ability of top management to tolerate ambiguity, differences of opinions, and new ideas. Since innovation is a process that can tap into an employee's subconscious and conscious associations, it is necessary to remove any obstacles that may impair their vision. One way to do this is to reward employees aggressively and rapidly, both as individuals and in groups. Rewards for innovation should cover the physical (good of the self), spiritual (good of the whole), and intellectual (good of the idea). These efforts should encourage the blossoming of continuous innovation within the corporate environment (see Figure 3-7).

Inspire employees to innovate. To inspire employees to innovate consistently, a company needs to foster an environment of creativity and not fear the short-term chaos that may result from these efforts. Creativity is the process by which we transform information, needs, and events into a long-term, cohesive product improvement strategy. Creativity is the value-added we impose on matter, energy, and information. Creativity energizes the ergonomic product improvement process and is essential if you want continuous innovation to be an aspect of your product development philosophy. Foremost in developing the fabric of creativity is the fiber of trust. Trust is the offspring of sincerity and gratitude for a job well done. Managers who fail to trust and understand creativity, who fail to tolerate ambiguity, who are more con-

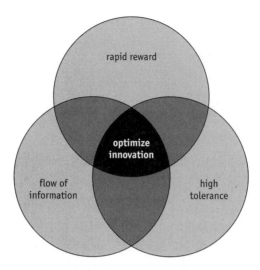

Figure 3-7. An Organization's Interaction with the Employee to Optimize Innovation

cerned about predetermined objectives than being leaders, block the flow of information and undermine the success of the product development team by defenestrating value before it is achieved. The organization's first vital steps in formulating the playing field for creativity and innovation are for the CEO and Board to determine what business the company is in, to state the corporate vision, and to inspire the organization to achieve this vision by developing and designing the appropriate products to fit that vision.

ERGONOMICS AND INDUSTRIAL DESIGN

When considering the relationship between ergonomics and industrial design, I'm reminded of a story about Samuel Clemens. He had nicked himself while shaving and reportedly let out a string of expletives with the style of a Mississippi steamboat captain. His wife responded, "Sam, I can't believe what you just said," and, having an excellent memory, she repeated the tirade exactly. Mr. Clemens replied, "My dear, you have the words, but not the music." In the development of modern products, ergonomics is analogous to the words and industrial design, the music. Separated, they leave each other incomplete.

Industrial design has yet to reinvent itself for the twenty-first century. The science of biomechanically-based ergonomics could be just the quantitative tool to assist industrial designers in creating superior products. The founding fathers of American industrial design, Raymond Lowey, Walter Darwin Teague, and Henry Dryfuss need a new evolutionary step to vitalize their postmodern idealism. The fusion of aesthetic sensibility with biomechanically-based ergonomics could provide a new vehicle and classification for product design professionals: *ergonomic product designers.* Of course, their training would require buttressing with biomechanics and other formal ergonomics courses, but this is not much of a problem considering the many good ergonomic course offerings in the U.S. and abroad. The Human Factors and Ergonomics Society in Santa Monica, California, is a good source for obtaining both graduate program information and capable ergonomics consultants seeking consumers for the specialized services they provide.

Product design is an activity that combines top-down and bottom-up thinking. The top-down way of solving design problems begins with a clear set of design rules and a well-established design method. This is what many experts do naturally, and hence, it is analogous to an expert system. Bottom-up design involves making need-based improvements without explicit rules or guidelines. It allows for creative leaps and often produces radically new ways of solving design problems. As Vora and Helandar (1992) point out, most design is probably a convergence of these two methods (see Figure 3-8).

ERGONOMICS AND DESIGN FOR MANUFACTURABILITY (DFG)

The application of ergonomic design ranges from product configuration and execution to manufacturing systems. The movement that has swept

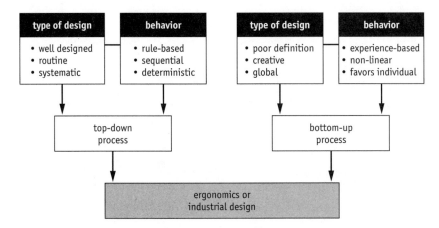

Figure 3-8. Some Tributaries for Ergonomic Industrial Design

through manufacturing, design for manufacturability (DFG), has largely ignored the use of ergonomics as a tool for reducing the cost of manufacture. But minimizing the cumulative exposures that contribute to musculoskeletal injuries would reduce manufacturing costs. The goal of DFG is the same as it is for product design, namely, creating the transparent interface between the employees and the tools that they use to construct products or perform services. Grossmith (1992) illustrates well the ergonomic considerations required to design for manufacturability (see Figure 3-9).

When addressed improperly, musculoskeletal stress results in increased operator fatigue, errors, soft tissue injuries, workers compensation, medical leave, lost time, restricted days, and so on. This all leads to a basic ergonomic rule:

> Company production, design, and mechanical and industrial engineers all must be knowledgeable in the application of ergonomics for both product development and production. This is a competitive advantage and a necessary step on the road to ergonomic quality.

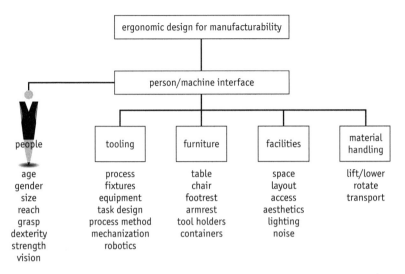

Figure 3-9. Ergonomic Considerations Required For Design for Manufacturability

To better understand the position of ergonomics in design for manufacturability it is helpful to view the competitive minimization forces. The goal is to minimize component costs, assembly costs, production costs, and interface stress simultaneously (see Figure 3-10).

PRODUCT DESIGN AND PRODUCT LIABILITY

New or improved products need to undergo rigorous safety analysis to help ensure they will not contribute to the development of an injury. Specifically, products need to be analyzed with regard to labels, warnings and operating instructions, packaging, servicing, and the assessment of impact on instantaneous and cumulative trauma disorders. As shown in Table 3-1, the number of product-related injuries treated in emergency rooms in the U.S. is alarmingly high.

Until recently, it was nearly impossible for ergonomics to assess the likelihood that a product will contribute to cumulative trauma. Today, the assessment is somewhat easier to make, though the situation is still

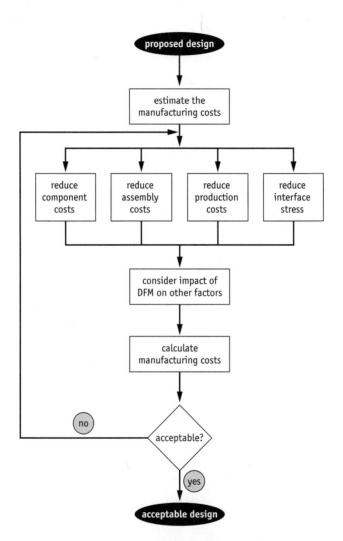

Figure 3-10. The Competitive Advantage in the Ergonomic Design for Manufacturing

not completely clear. An exact *dose-response* relationship is not known between cumulative exposures and the development of joint injuries such as back or wrist injuries. Currently, in our product ergonomics laboratory we are evaluating the relationship between wrist motions and

Table 3-1. Products with More Than 100,000 Annual Injuries

Product Group	Emergency Room Treated Injuries (000)
Stairs, ramps, landings, floors	1693
Cutlery, knives	449
Chairs, sofas and sofa beds	381
Beds, mattresses, pillows	363
Non-glass doors and panels	337
Tables	333
Nails, carpet tacks	242
Interior ceilings, walls and panels	228
Glass doors, windows and panels	218
Desks, cabinets, shelves and racks	210
Cans and other containers	209
Ladders and stools	179
Toys	164
Bath and shower structures	153
Workshop manual tools	119

changes in median nerve conduction velocity. As median nerve conduction velocity is a standard part of the diagnostic criteria for wrist injury, we want to see if it can be used to set cutoff limits for healthy wrist motion exposures.

Ergonomists can, however, measure the postures and forces that occur while using the product and compare them with those that have been associated with the development of cumulative trauma. Dr. William Marras at Ohio State University has conducted several studies of this type, which found that the magnitude of wrist acceleration during flexion and extension is related to the incidence of reported musculoskeletal injuries of the wrist. For office equipment, the starting document is the ANSI-HFES 100 Computer Workstation standard soon to be revised to ANSI-HFES 200. For manufacturing, the NIOSH Work Practices guide for manual materials handling and the *Draft Ergonomics Protection Standard (EPS)* from OSHA can serve as initial guidelines.

One of the best strategies a company can use for avoiding potential product liability associated with cumulative trauma is to optimize the comfort of the user. Comfort and cumulative injury occupy the same user response spectrum. Products that are comfortable to use are unlikely to generate cumulative forces that would produce a soft tissue injury over time. To optimize user acceptance and minimize significant potential injuries and liabilities an ergonomic assessment should be incorporated into all corporate product safety evaluations.

In the U.S., the performance of the product is scrutinized under strict tort liability. The plaintiff must prove that the product is defective, and the defendant is legally responsible for the defect if that defect caused harm to the plaintiff (Bralla, 1996). In general, defects are defined as those flaws that arise from the design of the product, those flaws that occur during the manufacturing of a product, and those flaws that result from improper or incomplete provision of user instructions or warnings. This approach supersedes the need to establish negligence. Regarding design defects, it is often necessary to establish what was known at the time the product was developed, or more precisely, what the state-of-the-art was with regard to the design process.

Each and every new product, therefore, should have a detailed ergonomic assessment (best-in-class analysis) for the intended user. Further, the assessments and their results should be carefully documented and interpreted in the context of the state-of-the-art of that particular product, or the industry standard. Product ergonomics expertise is usually needed to achieve this requirement.

As with many trade-offs, organizations may need to calculate the cost-benefit of the research and development (R&D) required to minimize the product's potential for harm. This does not, however, supersede the need or responsibility for care in protecting users from untoward results of product use. In Figure 3-11, Bralla (1996) presents a hierarchy to be considered for controlling potential hazards.

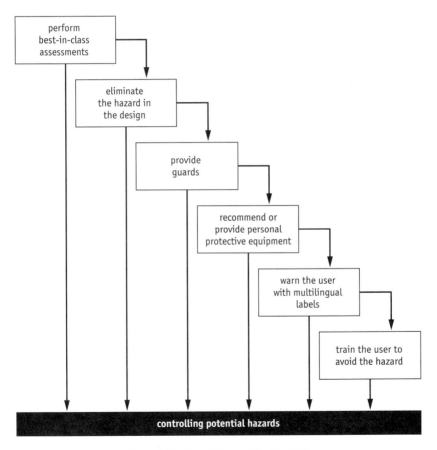

Figure 3-11. Hazard Minimization Hierarchy

WHAT YOU SHOULD KNOW

1. The ergonomic product development process is user-centered, both cognitively and physiologically.

2. The opportunity now exists for companies to gain significant market share by ensuring that all of their products are ergonomically best-in-class—a differentiation strategy based on optimizing user comfort and product fit.

3. The main asset of innovation-dependent companies is the knowledge worker. The success of the modern corporation depends upon this new class of innovators.

4. To encourage paradigm-shifting and paradigm-enhancing innovations in a company, enrich the availability and flow of information, reward innovation, and have a high toleration of ambiguity.

5. The fusion of aesthetic sensibility with biomechanically-based ergonomics could assist industrial designers in creating superior products.

6. Ergonomics design for manufacturability reduces the cost of manufacturing by reducing the potential costs of musculoskeletal injuries.

WHAT YOU SHOULD DO

1. Use ergonomic design for manufacturability to minimize component costs, assembly costs, and production costs while reducing cumulative exposures and improving customer satisfaction.

2. Perform a brutally objective evaluation of your corporate culture. Does it promote innovation? Does it reward innovation? Does it tolerate ambiguity? Is the flow of information about your business and customers plentiful and available?

3. Use a detailed ergonomic assessment (best-in-class analysis) to reduce product liability.

4

ergonomic products with a high IQ

> The whole of science is nothing more than a
> refinement of everyday thinking.
> —A.EINSTEIN, *PHYSICS AND REALITY* (1936)

PRODUCTS THAT ADAPT INTELLIGENTLY TO THE USER

To help ensure the success of new products, customer service must be properly combined with the product. Because microprocessor-based products have the inherent advantage of bringing information directly to their users, it is now possible to bundle customer service as part of the product itself. Customer service for such products means tailoring each automated, interactive product to best meet the demands of the user. This gives these products a kind of intelligence in the product-customer service interaction. Products are intelligent if they make and execute decisions for the benefit of their users. For intelligent products that come in contact with the human body, the opportunity exists to design products that automatically adapt to the customer on an ongoing basis. To do this effectively, the product design must include a rudimentary ergonomic knowledge of the customer-product interface.

The benefits of manufacturing an ergonomic product with a high IQ rather than one that lacks ergonomic awareness and intelligence are many:

- Product development cycles are shorter and less expensive due to changing product features through changes in software.

- Increased user acceptance and comfort result from products that easily and automatically adapt themselves to different body types, circumstances, and conditions of use.

- The ability to change the product feature response curve to fit unique and different customer demands improves product performance. Intelligent products are dynamic, as they may be designed so they can change over time.

- Low-cost software enhancement upgrades of products are within existing product platforms.

PRODUCT DEVELOPMENT: SIMPLICITY VS. ADJUSTABILITY

The basic design problem that intelligent products address and solve is the customer requirement for simplicity and adjustability. In traditional product development programs, simplicity and flexibility are at odds with each other. A manufacturer wants the product to be simple to increase reliability and ease of use, and to minimize development costs. As the complexity of a product increases, so do the number of potential interactions between parts or subsystems (see Figure 4-1).

The number of interactions increases rapidly when you add more elements such as parts or program steps to the product. Interestingly, as the number of elements increases, so does the need for reduced error rates in each element for the product to be error free or nearly so. Therefore, even small increases in the number of elements such as parts,

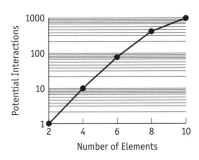

Figure 4-1. Number of Interactions as a Function of the Number of Elements

components, and modules, result not only in vastly increased interactions that require analysis, testing, evaluation, and management review, but also necessitate that all components, of both newer and older design, now have to be built to a more exacting standard. In the best of all possible worlds this means that more time is spent and greater costs are incurred during product development. This is why simplicity of product design and construction has traditionally been the key concept influencing all other decisions regarding the development of the product.

However, flexibility, or adjustability, is also a desired feature—one that enables the product to be designed to fit and perform properly for a wide range of user attributes. Usually the design team compromises some product adjustability to maintain simplicity and a given price. This minimizes how involved an active user can be in adjusting and interacting with the product interface.

One way to negate the ease of use and flexibility logjam is to develop microprocessor-based, intelligent products. Microprocessors are evolving at a biological growth rate. The processing speed doubles every eighteen months. Within 25 years, according to David Patterson (1995), one microcomputer will be as powerful as all the microprocessors in Silicon Valley today combined (see Figure 4-2).

Regardless of the actual multiple in power, the calculating improve-

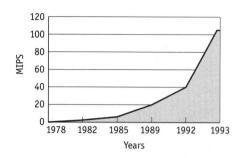

Figure 4-2. Growth of Microprocessor Power Over Time

ment of computers will be undeniable. Soon companies will be using the microprocessor in real time to dramatically reshape the interface between people and products. This intelligent product-interface will reside at the surface of the body, for example in the case of beds, chairs, and clothing. More dramatically, it will increasingly rest beneath the surface, or within the body, as would be the case for intelligent bones, solid state replacements for the retina, *in vivo* drug delivery systems, telemetric replacement nervous systems, artificial muscle, and solid state memory enhancements. One thing is certain—in the future the power of the computer will obliterate the issue of simplicity versus adjustability.

INGREDIENTS OF A HIGH IQ PRODUCT

To be intelligent, a product has to be able to gather pertinent information about the user and respond accordingly. The common denominator for products that come into contact with the human body is the need for an ergonomics algorithm to drive the user interface. The decision-making aspects of these algorithms may be determined from best-in-class assessments. The results of these assessments may then be used to develop the control logic, programming, and firmware for this new class of intelligent products. Even the most rudimentary intelligent products require computational power to collect and prioritize information to modify the product interface; hence the need for software.

The business of producing intelligent products requires the fusion of *analog* and digital measurement. The world is analog, yet computational power is digital. For example, the continuous measurement domains of pressure, joint force, sound, light intensity, and acceleration require responsive and continuous sensing. For these continuous measurement domains an analog of the activity needs to be created, then digitized for processing. Such is the case with vehicle accelerometers, which provide the input for air bag activation. Therefore, processing speed alone does not provide the means for human capability to transform to a higher level. An analog revolution must occur as well. One of the current leaders in the development of analog devices is National Semiconductor Corporation's CEO, Dr. Gilbert Amelio. Peter Elstrom (1995) has quoted Dr. Amelio regarding the upcoming watershed:

One of the characteristics of the future technology is the humanization element. Mankind has always developed tools to better our lives and increase our productivity. With National Semiconductor technology, we will be able to connect people to our electronic tools in increasingly harmonious ways.

Cognition and Memory

The ultimate transparent interface and intelligent product would be one that directly communicates between products and the brain or nervous system. Recently, Dr. Fromherz (1995) has reported success in stimulating and controlling a single neuron with a silicon chip. Researchers elsewhere have been able to induce a current flow in a neuron with an adjacent electromagnetic field. No current actually flowed between the silicon and the cell. It is now possible to detect and stimulate neuron activity with a single piece of silicon. It is only a matter of time before direct silicon-based brain-to-PC interfaces are developed, giving new meaning to the term "intelligent products." For example, in the twenty-first century, brain prostheses to augment memory or the senses may be as common as eyeglasses. When combined with 3-D holographic memory, silicon brain interfaces could offer an entirely new generation of human-centered products.

Current compact discs (CDs) can hold about 660 million bytes of data (300,000 pages of text or 80 minutes of music). With current data compression techniques, CD storage can be expanded to hold 700 to 1,000 million bytes depending on the data format (courtesy of EWB Inc., Carlsbad, California). Using semiconductor lasers and information compression techniques, data may be expanded to tens of billions of bytes within five years (Psaltis and Mok, 1995). To store hundreds of billions of bytes, 3-D holographic storage devices are likely to be required. These devices would be able to transfer data at greater than one billion bits per second and select a randomly chosen element in one hundred millionths of a second.

What's the big need for memory and speed? Simple. Computers, like many great tools, are modeled after nature—in this case the model is the human brain. Our sense organs just so happen to register about one billion bits per second. Of these billion bits, 3 million make it to the nerve junction, whereupon 16 enter our conscious awareness and 0.7 leave a lasting impression in our memories (Grandjean, 1995). With a small array of 3-D holographic memories, everything our bodies see and feel during 16 waking hours could be stored (about 57 trillion bits) and rapidly retrieved at will. Undoubtedly, virtual reality efforts would prosper under such fidelity.

Virtual reality as a transparent interface. Virtual reality is computer-enhanced experience that provides an ergonomic bridge between human desires and computational power. Successful enhancement of virtual reality requires a transparent interface. In fact, a transparent interface is the whole point of virtual reality as the next evolutionary step for human computing. Manufacturers who incorporate virtual technology will have to embrace ergonomic technology to ensure a powerful leveraging of the human sense organs. Brenda Laurel (1995) beautifully expresses the bridge between human senses and computational power as the evolutionary step in resolving the separateness of the mind and body:

> People have until now thought of computers as the last stop on the road of mind-body dualism: as close to disembodied thought as the material world permits. Computers generally have no sense organs, nor do they address human senses particularly well. They have evolved as a race of severed heads, doomed by the arcana of their communications mechanisms to make extremely small talk with people who are almost as strange as they are. VR (virtual reality), in contrast, makes little or no distinction between body and mind. Instead it employs in a new context the bodily senses that evolution has so magnificently prepared.

Interestingly, the total elimination of the interface has the potential to upgrade virtual reality to reality. Do contact lenses produce virtual corrected vision or corrected vision? Implantable or wearable devices that allow for near complete acclimation induce a synthesis of the real and the virtual that is inextricably interwoven. The result is the humanization or human absorption of technology.

Reaction Time

In addition to cognition and memory, reaction time plays a significant role in determining human performance and limitations. Reaction time is defined as that interval of time between the receipt of information and the required response (see Figure 4-3).

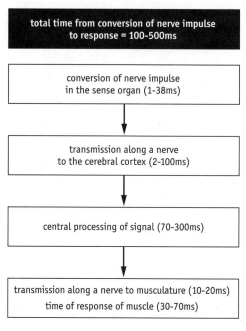

Figure 4-3. Reaction Time Distribution

Most of our reaction time is spent processing signals rather than reacting physically. Theoretically, we can speed up reaction time by a factor of five by using really fast (relative to biological standards) signal processors combined with our neuromuscular system or an augmented one. The potential to use this technology to overcome congenital or trau-matagenically-induced brain injuries is fantastic. Though it may sound futuristic, intelligent biocomputer replacement parts, or what may be called the business of developing internal tools to assist the mind and body, will be very big business in the next fifty years.

PRACTICAL APPLICATIONS OF INTELLIGENT PRODUCTS

The interface between the customer and the product must be responsive to the changing needs of the user, possess dynamic characteristics, and be versatile within a specified range of adjustments. Ergonomics defines the parameters of the customer interface under all possible conditions of use. In addition to creating a transparent interface for the user, intelligent products can accentuate product performance under varied conditions. The range of intelligent products that come into contact with the body is limitless. The following categories illustrate the power of this technology.

Medical footwear. Intelligent shoes could be developed that would allow the plantar surface of the shoe to automatically change its shape to better fit the individual. This could be achieved if the footwear can sense the loads on the foot and instruct the innersole, under microprocessor control, to change its shape with the use of electrical charge or pneumatic pressure. In the case of the diabetic, this could mean forestalling or preventing the development of decubitus ulcers through the distribution of forces to more robust parts of the foot over time. Ulcers of this type are currently responsible for approximately 50,000 leg amputations in the U.S. annually. The same technology could be applied to wheelchairs to help prevent pressure sores that result from prolonged contact to insensate or immobile parts of the body.

Vehicular seats. Intelligent vehicular seats could help immensely in increasing comfort while sitting, especially for longer periods of time. The seat surface could sense the load distribution pattern that the passenger imposes on it. From this load distribution pattern it is possible to

recognize distinct comfort levels. Mechanically or pneumatically changing the shape of the seat surface to better fit the user would enhance
comfort levels. When a person sits down, the ischial tuberosities (the
bones at the base of the pelvis) come into contact with the seat pan as a
result of the rotation of the pelvis and thigh. This causes an accompa-
nying flattening or derotation of the lumbar spine by approximately 38
degrees. This flattening increases intradiscal pressure, resulting in
discomfort over time. As the spinal discs are 70 to 90 percent water, this
increased pressure flattens the disk and thereby reduces its load-carry-
ing capabilities. An intelligent seat could be programmed to detect this
flattening in the form of a pressure distribution pattern and restore the
proper amount of lost lordosis (low back curve) with a like change in the
seat back curvature. For example, on long drives, an intelligent seat
could gradually help restore the progressively flattening curvature of the
spine that results from muscle fatigue and mechanical creep of the soft
tissues.

Neck support. Like the back, forces and torque on the cervical spine
(neck) can vary greatly as a result of small changes in neck angle (see
Figure 4-4). With the neck in the forward bent position the neck torque
increases from 1.2 Nm in the neutral position to 3.7 Nm (Newton-meters,
a measure of torque, like foot-pounds in the English system of units).
Adequate neck support for a vehicle seat has yet to be developed, despite
the fact that the weight of the head is about seven percent of overall
body weight and the static postural load it imposes on the spine can
cause severe discomfort while performing seated tasks. Who hasn't had
a stiff neck after a long drive?

Body supports. Intelligent body supports could greatly expand the
range of loads that the body can safely handle while performing various
tasks. Back supports, for example, could be constructed to sense loads on
the spine and automatically increase their stiffness to facilitate exoskele-

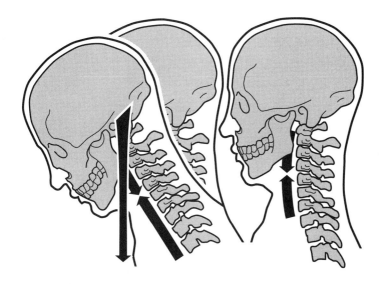

Figure 4-4. Slight Changes in Neck Position Produce Significant Changes in Spinal Torque

tal load transmission, thereby decreasing the likelihood of spinal damage. The medical application for intelligent body supports also extends to casts and braces of every type. With imbedded microprocessor-based technology, a leg brace could sense the deviation of the knee or ankle and limit the range of motion to an acceptable level.

As these examples illustrate, intelligence could be added to almost any product that comes into contact with the body, empowering the product to adapt automatically to ever-changing consumer needs. Development of these products depends largely on quantifying the relationship between the product and the users' comfort, safety, and performance. As microprocessor speed and power increase, the number and sophistication of intelligent products that address and quantify this relationship will also increase. This will enable the development of a world of dynamic products whose characteristics will constantly change and adapt under conditions of use. The net effect of products that contain these intelligent sense-adjustment capabilities will be the maintenance of customer fit and satisfaction for longer periods of the product use cycle.

ADDING INTELLIGENCE TO EXISTING PRODUCTS

Upgrading existing products will require substantial time and monetary costs for a company, much of which would be focused on the production of prototypes and changes in the tooling required to produce the improved product. Within a given product platform, however, intelligent products may be designed to allow for software-based product enhancements on the existing platform. For example, in the case of intelligent beds, it is possible to develop an upgrade strategy that would counteract the foam creep during years of regular use by incorporating a software upgrade for the microprocessor-controlled inflatable surface. It is conceivable that such upgrades could be downloaded into the product with either physical modules, such as chip-on-a-card technology, or telemetrically with infrared, optical, or RF transmitters.

The benefit of this type of product improvement strategy for a company is the dramatically lower cost of enhancing a specific product. The development of intelligent products will also require even traditional manufacturers, such as those who make automobile seats and beds, to become, in part, software focused. Additionally, intelligence applied to traditional products may enhance how these products can be upgraded without wholesale replacement. This could create additional synergy with the green movement to minimize waste and recycling.

PRODUCTS FOR THE ELDERLY AND THE PHYSICALLY CHALLENGED

As the number of people over 65 continues to grow, and the physically challenged become more mobile and productive, a significant segment of all product categories will consist of products designed to fulfill the needs of this segment of the population. Many of these products will be high IQ products that will give users more mobility, control, and ease of use. For this class of products, ergonomic superiority means fitness for use, in addition to ease of use. EQ combined with products with high IQs may yet be the most powerful tool we can develop to negate the Darwinistic *survival of the fittest* and replace it with performance by design. For example, people who need assistance controlling their muscles could benefit from products such as multichannel, evoked-potential interfaces that would control implanted neuromuscular stimulators.

Not long ago I read about a group of ergonomists at Wright Patterson Airforce Base in Ohio who were experimenting with alternative means of aircraft control (not using hands or feet), especially during high G maneuvers. They were using what is known as EEG-evoked potentials to control the acquisition of a target on the screen, as well as the positive/negative roll of an aircraft simulator. With a great deal of excitement I arranged to meet with Dr. Grant McMillian, the Director of this important research project. I was placed in the cockpit of the aircraft simulator with two electrodes connected to my scalp on one end and a locking amplifier-simulator stepping motor on the other. McMillian's assistant then came over and said, "Now I'm going to coach you—think left" (enhance the evoked potential), at which point the simulator started to roll to the left. Thinking "right" was more difficult until I was able to feel through the biofeedback—the action of suppressing the evoked potential in the visual cortex. Then someone who was trained at this gave a demonstration. It was amazing how adept he was. With practice you can control (think) the proper moves much more readily. What Dr. McMillian has shown is that evoked potential control of external devices and muscles is accurate, repeatable, and will probably improve with traditional conditioning or training efforts.

While this technology has the potential to control interfaces when musculature is difficult to move, as in a 7G turn, another application may be to control muscles with implantable electrical stimulators. In this case the brain actually contracts the muscles telemetrically instead of through the original biological route. One such potential for this technology is in helping people with paralyzed body parts activate their muscles.

PRODUCTS THAT SELL THEMSELVES

Though people try out many products that come into contact with the body before they buy them, in shopping malls, boutiques, and other traditional mass distribution channels, the salespeople are not often well trained to demonstrate and adjust a product to a prospective customer. Adding intelligence to your products offers the advantage of automatic self-adjustment, by which the product adjusts itself to fit the customer during these brief, but valuable evaluation periods. This greatly enhances the showroom feel, leading the customer to perceive a real difference in your product (product differentiation) that should translate into greater sales. One could envision the unique experience of trying out smart beds in a furniture showroom.

WHAT YOU SHOULD KNOW

1. Intelligent products often result in shorter product development cycles, increased user acceptance, improved performance, and reduction in the cost and time to upgrade.

2. Intelligent products solve the fundamental problem of providing for both the customer's need for simplicity and their desire for adjustability.

3. Virtual reality is the ergonomic bridge between human desire and computational power.

WHAT YOU SHOULD DO

1. In conjunction with your product development team, customers, and associates, select the first product or product category to make intelligent. Inspire the team to build their first intelligent product this year.

5

ergonomic quality and concurrent engineering

When there is something to be done,
the world knows how to get it done.
—R. W. EMERSON (1860)

Concurrent engineering (CE) is the parallel performance of market research, design, development, and production planning. It is the combination of efforts and disciplines, brought together within a multifunctional team. Basically, with CE in place, various company teams use real-time feedback in their planning and execution. The effect is threefold:

1. Compressed product development cycles

2. Better system integration, design for manufacturability, and customer satisfaction

3. Lower overall development and production costs

CE is, in essence, the intentional blurring of the distinctions among marketing, design, development, and production. Everyone in the organization is now responsible for the success of the entire project, and for communicating their role, needs, preferences, trade-offs, experiences, and expertise.

COMMUNICATION IN A CE ENVIRONMENT

With CE, the organization's management information flows through three major groups: the business group, product engineering group, and production engineering group (see Figure 5-1). The business group consists of management, marketing, sales, and customer service. The product engineering group consists of project management, product engineering, ergonomics, industrial design, and product research. And the production engineering group consists of plant engineering, production engineering, ergonomics, maintenance, and principal vendors of manufacturing

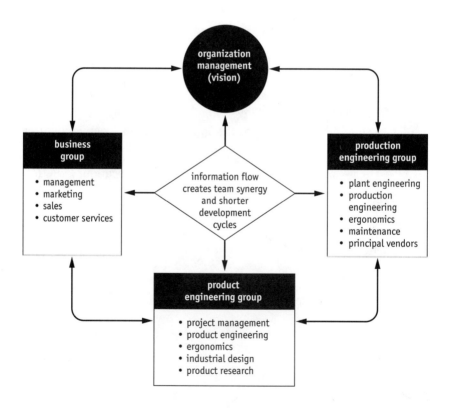

Figure 5-1. Concurrent Engineering Development Cycle

equipment and components. When the flow of communication is good, the result is team synergy and shorter development cycles. Like most process management tools, the success of CE depends on the corporate style and culture. However, for CE to succeed properly, senior management needs to openly commit to the process, yet at the same time, have a hands-off approach to the multifunctional team.

With changing social and economic environments, as well as changing consumer trends due to the constant pace of technological innovation, companies must make rapid changes in industrial processes to keep abreast. Specifically, the need to develop new products is crucial to survival. This is why it is imperative that companies translate customer needs and specifications into a product as quickly as possible. But, this does not mean rushing headlong into prototypes.

CE's approach is to spend more time defining and specifying the product in the early concept stages so that the majority of modifications are made at the design stage, well before prototype or preproduction cycles. Part of this process is to build customer expectations into the design of the product. In fact, customers define the product in their own words, and that description is translated into engineering specifications. Quality function deployment (QFD), which defines the product in the customers' voice, is discussed further in chapter 6.

For CE to operate smoothly, good communication between the customer and the different groups in the team is essential. To facilitate this, CE requires the use of networked design and development tools and computer-aided design (CAD). It is important to be able to simulate many alternatives to a design as early as possible. This simulation process often translates into early visualization of products and digital human models. For this, human-computer-aided design software is essential. The way a customer uses a product can be partially simulated as a digital mock-up. For example, you can determine the strength, reach, and range of motion a user requires while using a product. Other CAD, graphics, analysis, and communications programs are also essential for analyzing and communicating between prototype and critical design decisions. Smaller companies can use personal computers that run CAD programs effectively. By linking individual workstations with a server and networks, companies can send and receive data from vendors and customers worldwide.

CE requires senior management's commitment to new technology and customer-centered product development. Though American companies like the Big Three—Chrysler, Ford, and General Motors—have been adopting some CE principles since the mid-eighties, this approach to project management is still relatively new. After a shaky start in the U.S., CE is now starting to pay off, as companies like Xerox, Digital Equipment, and the Big Three make great strides in reducing time-to-market and in regaining market share (Hartley, 1992).

SYNERGY OF CE AND ERGONOMIC QUALITY

A successful CE effort benefits from both ergonomic quality and QFD. While CE combines interdepartment disciplines to create a multifunctional team and flow of information, EQ combines and synthesizes the interdisciplinary sciences (medicine, mathematics, physics, engineering, physiology, biomechanics, and psychology). This provides the added innovative muscle—keeping abreast of new developments and trends in these interdisciplines that can be infused into the new product/service. This makes ergonomics an especially powerful tool for business, engineering, and production teams. If positioned properly, ergonomics can become the *cause celebre* to rally the organization into making great, state-of-the-art, easy-to-use products. The combination of CE and ergonomics can most readily be seen by viewing the product development tools (see Figure 5-2).

Figure 5-2. CE and EQ Product Development Tools

The primary concern with CE and ergonomics is keeping the customer in the product development loop, whether that customer is the individual who buys your product or service or the vendor who builds or supplies your product or service. Figure 5-3 shows how ergonomics is the common denominator among the three tributaries that feed the final product/service delivery in the CE process. With this model the customer is assured of being primary throughout the parallel product development process.

CE and EQ fit neatly together in many ways. Besides emphasizing the all-important task of assessing and building in customer needs and

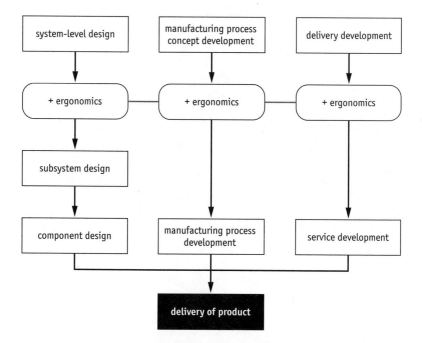

Figure 5-3. Parallel Process for CE and Ergonomics

expectations, these two systems have the following features in common. They:

- Focus on quality from the start of the product development cycle.

- Compress the product development cycle to shorten time-to-market of improved products.

- Use networked design, CAD, and other development tools to simulate as many alternatives to a design as possible.

- Reduce the number of prototype repetitions prior to finalizing the design specification.

- Improve communication in the product development process, thereby utilizing the full talents of a company's manufacturing engineers, as well as removing many of the miscommunication glitches that traditionally occur between production and manufacturing—glitches that can cause many serious foul-ups in prototype designs.

- Require senior management to commit to a customer-centered product development approach.

- Use a multifunctional team approach to product development.

- Create an interactive, creative environment in which innovation can flourish.

Ergonomics Enhances CE

To be successful, CE requires significant investments in technology and communication systems. An organization considering CE has an excellent opportunity to embark on human-computer-aided design as well. The use of photo-realistic, digital-human models for articulating and evaluating products is a good start. All three groups in the team (business, product engineering, and production) need to evaluate the customer-product interactions as early, as quickly, and as accurately as possible to provide a smooth flow of information and improved development progress. Sales, production engineering, and product engineering should work together to achieve a parallel process for integrating ergonomics into the CE process during product development.

WHAT YOU SHOULD KNOW

1. CE is the parallel performance of all of the essential steps of product development.

2. The benefit of CE and ergonomics together is reduced time and cost for product/service development, as well as improved synergy across corporate teams.

3. Successful CE requires a significant investment in software to provide CAD/CAM/Human-CAD and improved communications among what may be highly separated work groups.

4. When a company adds EQ to the CE product development process, the development team is able to more accurately turn the all-important customer voice into an engineering reality.

WHAT YOU SHOULD DO

1. Have an expert evaluate the state of your current CE-ergonomics product development programs for the purpose of identifying strengths and weaknesses.

6

EQ, QFD, and ISO 9000

It is the mark of good action
that it appears inevitable in retrospect.
—ROBERT LOUIS STEVENSON

Sometimes the obvious is embraced fairly late, for example, personal traits that indicate good character, such as the ability to listen well. Quality function deployment (QFD) is a team strategy to develop and operate a system that feeds customer preferences back into product and service specifications. It has become known as the "voice of the customer" in product development. Broadly speaking, QFD means deployment of quality through deployment of quality functions. For many companies QFD cut in half problems encountered at the beginning stages of product development and reduced development time by one-half to one-third. QFD also helped to ensure customer satisfaction and increase sales.

QFD—ANALOG TO ERGONOMIC QUALITY

QFD is perfectly analogous to ergonomic quality in that its goal is to optimize customer satisfaction and performance, including safety and comfort. QFD teams seek to ask the tough question—what does the customer want? The goal is to satisfy customers by translating their demands into design targets and major quality assurance points to be used throughout the production stage. Often customers can only provide rudimentary feedback on traditional questionnaires and in focus groups, such as, "this product needs a better handle." In the case of ergonomic features, it is up to the ergonomic development team to extract that better handle design through structured, best-in-class assessments, where the customer *speaks* through muscles, joints, and other quantitative interface assessments. EQ and QFD assess customer needs and produce customer delight through proactive, deterministic assessments and improvements. These assessments may be controlled, time-specified, and in general, used strategically to improve products rapidly. The sustainable, dual goal here is product/service quality improvements in compressed development time frames. All other factors being equal, the shorter the development time, the more successful the product.

Other sources of feedback, such as customer complaints, lawsuits, and international standards are off-line feedback elements for the EQ and QFD process, and while important, are secondary sources of information for customer-product assessments. For the EQ and QFD process to be successful, a real-time flow of communication must be established between customer assessments and all members of the development team, including engineering, industrial design, sales, marketing, management, and finance. Brossert (1991) describes the house of quality concept (see page 95 for futher discussion) as a simplistic, but useful, approach to translate customer recommendations into engineering specifications. It replaces the hierarchical design decision with a customer-driven one. This strategy is useful when implementing a bottoms-up approach to product development.

THE QFD QUALITY PROCESS

QFD is a structured process for converting customer needs and desires into product specifications. It is the instructional theme for market-driven products and uses four major planning tools (Mears, 1995):

1. *The customer requirements planning matrix.* Translates customer needs into product characteristics. For ergonomic house of quality, performs best-in-class assessments to determine ergonomic requirements to satisfy the customer.

2. *The product characteristics deployment matrix.* Translates product characteristics into critical component characteristics.

3. *Process plan and quality control charts.* Identify critical points, decisions, and steps.

4. *Operating instructions.* Identify next steps for success.

Once the above information is acquired, it is possible to construct a house of quality matrix.

HOUSE OF ERGONOMIC QUALITY

The QFD house of quality is a *graphical procedure for converting customer needs and goals into product specifications.* The house of ergonomic quality, however, is a *system for quantifying the relationship between the customer's need and the product features.* To achieve this in a simple and structured way, determine an engineering characteristic (for example, speed, sharpness, or weight) for every customer requirement. Sometimes the customer requirements are general, for example, the product needs to be lightweight, whereas the technical descriptor must be more specific, for example, density, rigidity, hardness of the plastic case, and location of the center of mass. Measurement of these refined attributes is necessary to define the customer's need precisely with regard to each engineering characteristic.

In short, the QFD house of quality is a product development procedure to help the product development team prioritize and evaluate customer needs with measurements that the team is familiar with. While the house of ergonomic quality is similar in intent and results to traditional house of quality programs, the difference is that the technical descriptors are evaluated within an ergonomic best-in-class analysis that focuses on assessing and minimizing the human-product interface. By fiat, companies that perform ergonomic house of quality assessments create for themselves a strategic advantage by targeting customer needs with fewer prototypes. The dual advantage is shortened time-to-market and extraordinary customer delight.

ERGONOMICS QUALITY AND ISO 9000

> We stand today on the edge of a new frontier...
> But the new frontier of which I speak is not a
> set of promises—it is a set of challenges.
> —JOHN F. KENNEDY (1960)

Some seventy countries have adopted ISO 9000 standards as their country standard. ISO 9000 is, in the strict sense, the first global comprehensive standard for industry and has become the de facto entrance fee for doing business worldwide. To become certified as an ISO 9000-approved supplier, an approved registrar must evaluate your manufacturing/service system and find it in compliance (see Figure 6-1).

There are five standards included in the ISO 9000 series (Besterfield et al., 1995):

1. "ISO 9000 Quality Management and Quality Assurance
   Standards Guidelines for Selection and Use." This part
   defines terms and provides directions for use and application of the series.

2. "ISO 9001 Quality Systems Model for Quality Assurance in
   Design and Development." This is the full-blown ISO series

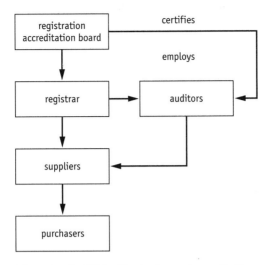

Figure 6-1. The ISO Certification Process Assures Quality

that defines what quality is across the entire organization. This part contains 20 elements that need to be documented and approved.

3. "ISO 9002 Quality Systems Model for Quality Assurance in Production and Installation." Covers 18 of the 20 elements of the full program.

4. "ISO 9003 Quality Systems Model for Quality Assurance in Final Inspection and Test." Covers 12 of the 18 elements of ISO 9000.

5. "ISO 9004 Quality Management and Quality Systems Elements Guidelines." An overview of the series with evaluation guidelines.

There are many benefits to ISO 9000 registration, not the least of which is the establishment of an internationally accepted standard for the design, development, and production of products and services. ISO

9000 companies have reported strong gains in internal efficiency and international product sales as well (see Figure 6-2).

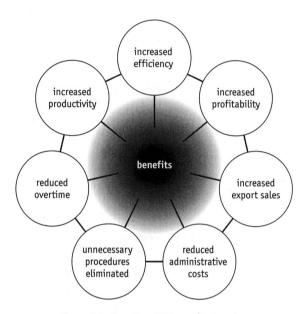

Figure 6-2. Benefits of ISO 9000 Registration

Fusing Ergonomics with ISO 9000

To obtain ISO 9000 certification it is advisable to implement an ergonomic system for both product development and production. In the product development phase, ergonomics should be incorporated into the Design Control step of ISO 9000. This step requires establishing and maintaining procedures to ascertain that a product or service is safe to use and meets users' requirements and the resulting design specifications. For production applications, ISO requirements dealing with process control, inspection and testing, handling, storage, packaging and delivery, and training need to incorporate ergonomic elements to achieve optimal productivity and safety in a state-of-the-art production control system. As Figure 6-3 demonstrates, the implementation responsibilities for ISO and ergonomics are nearly identical.

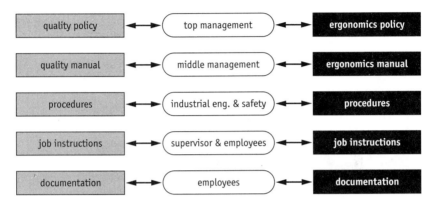

Figure 6-3. Comparison Between ISO 9000 and Ergonomics Program Implementation Responsibility

It is becoming increasingly difficult to be a world class competitor without ISO 9000 certification. Incorporating an ergonomics program in your product development and production areas also helps your company meet the qualifications for ISO 9000 certification.

Preparing for ISO 14000

Today environmental issues are commanding worldwide attention. With the release of the new ISO 14000 international standards for Environmental Management Systems (EMS) by the ISO/TC 207 technical committee, companies can now be certified for the environmental quality aspects of their products, processes, and services. Quality management and environmental management concepts share the preventive approach of the quality system as well as its continuous support and improvement by internal audits, management reviews, and corrective and preventive actions. The compatibility between the specifications of EMS and the quality system requirements facilitates the implementation of EMS by companies that already operate a quality system (Todorov, 1996). Since both the ISO 9000 and ISO 14000 share common system management principles, fusing an ergonomics program with ISO 9000 certification is also an excellent way to help companies prepare for and obtain certification with ISO 14000.

WHAT YOU SHOULD KNOW

1. QFD and EQ are perfectly analogous in their goal of providing customer satisfaction through optimizing a product's performance, safety, and comfort.

2. QFD is a structured process for converting customer needs into product specifications. EQ is a system for quantifying the relationship between customer needs and product features.

3. The house of ergonomic quality differs from the traditional house of quality programs by evaluating the technical descriptors within an ergonomic best-in-class analysis.

4. To be a world class competitor you must have ISO 9000 and ISO 14000 certification.

WHAT YOU SHOULD DO

1. Target your customer's needs and goals by performing an ergonomic house of quality assessment.

2. Implement an ergonomics quality program as part of your ISO 9000 and ISO 14000 initiative.

7

reducing workplace injuries with EQ

> Men should be taught as if you taught them not
> and things unknown proposed as things forgot.
> —A. POPE, (1711) AN ESSAY ON CRITICISM

WORKPLACE ERGONOMICS

Workplace ergonomics is the science of designing workplace tasks and tools to best fit the worker. The dual goal of workplace ergonomics is to optimize the performance of the worker as well as reduce the potential for injury. In the case of performance, companies often have to make a leap of faith when it comes to recognizing that the application of ergonomics can actually increase workplace productivity. Anecdotal cases have been presented throughout this book because there are so few controlled studies that document changes in productivity that follow the application of ergonomic principles. It is reasonable to assume that using ergonomics principles positively impacts productivity. In some cases, this impact is similar to a continuous improvement program that improves the efficiency of a workstation, which in turn, improves the productivity of the worker. However, this chapter focuses on the more readily measurable benefits of ergonomics, namely, reducing workplace injuries and how preventing cumulative workplace injuries seems to lie squarely in the purview of modern ergonomists.

Cumulative Trauma Disorders (CTD)

Since the implementation of the Occupational Safety and Health Act of 1970, the frequency and severity of most workplace injuries in the U.S. have decreased consistently. Implementation of proper safety practices has dramatically reduced injuries associated with instantaneous trauma. During the same period, non-impact, cumulative trauma disorders (CTD) have risen from a barely significant amount in 1970 to over 64 percent of all occupational illnesses in the U.S. in 1994 (see figure 7-1). This epidemic rise in injuries has surprised the professional occupational medicine and safety communities.

In 1982, I met with the plant manager of the 100,000-plus employee Anshan Iron and Steel Works in mainland China. Seeing the heavy manual labor performed, I had politely asked him about the back

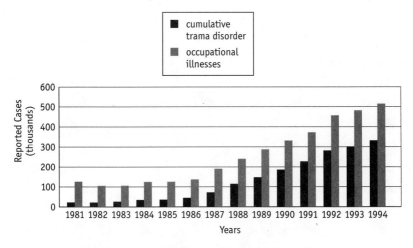

Figure 7-1. Reported Incidences of Cumulative Trauma Disorders

injuries his facility had experienced in the previous year. He laughed. "What is so funny?" I asked him. He answered, "We don't have the luxury to focus on back pain and injury. We have a 200-bed hospital, right here in the plant, where we are doing everything possible to address the near death, disabling, amputation, and severe burn type injuries. Back injuries may be present, but they don't warrant significant attention when compared to other, more pressing problems."

His response has helped me to understand what has happened in the U.S. and the West in general, with regard to cumulative musculoskeletal injuries. The reduced instances of instantaneously traumatogenic injuries has allowed the cumulative, slow-developing, gradually disabling injuries to come to the fore. Of course, the increase in reported frequency of these injuries may also be due to the greater awareness and ability to diagnose the injuries, the increased productivity demands of many businesses, which increase repetition rates of manufacturing processes, and the increased prevalence of women and older employees in the workforce.

The basic concept behind workplace ergonomics is that reducing both physical and psychological stress on the body (by improving employee comfort) is very likely to reduce workplace injuries. Physical and cognitive work require an interaction between people and machines. The four aspects of the person-machine system are the person, the interface, the machine, and the environment (see Figure 7-2).

Human capabilities should match the job at hand and when these four aspects are in harmony, injury potential is minimized, if not eliminated. In manufacturing for example, an inappropriate workstation layout may lead to cumulative musculoskeletal stress, as well as decreased productivity. The extent of the potential mismatch between worker and workstation may be evaluated with a quantitative workplace assessment, designed to identify and quantify the workplace stressors.

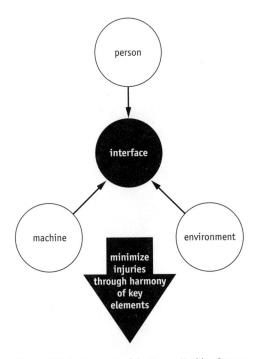

Figure 7-2. Key Elements of the Person-Machine System

The Role of Biomechanics in Workplace Ergonomics

So, why do cumulative workplace injuries lie in the purview of modern ergonomists, when a heretofore successful occupational medicine and safety community is available to look at the problems? The answer is surprisingly simple. For the most part, the etiology of cumulative musculoskeletal injuries consists of these four elements (see figure 7-12, page 128):

- force
- frequency
- posture
- vibration exposures

The best way to understand how these exposures affect the body is to measure the biomechanics of the interaction between the worker and the activity. Biomechanics is the only discipline that, over time, can quantify forces on and within the human body while it is engaged in work. However, education in biomechanical principles and measurement techniques, with few exceptions, is all but absent in traditional safety and occupational medicine curricula. This has fostered the need for experts in workplace ergonomics. As mentioned in Chapter 1, in traditional manufacturing, personnel departments overlook issues of safety and health, while production or research development departments concern themselves with manufacturing and design. Biomechanically-based ergonomics provides a company the opportunity to deal with these two areas, or departments, at one and the same time. In the case of manufacturing, the connections between safety, health, and design are all the more explicit and obvious.

It Begins with the Muscles

Interestingly, the traditional occupational health and safety approach is to minimize the exposure to *toxic agents*. How does traditional occupational health and safety handle the toxic exposure of cumulative musculoskeletal injuries? They really don't monitor these kinds of injuries until they occur. Why? Because biomechanically monitoring and quantifying the cumulative forces on the muscles is a major departure in subject matter for the occupational health specialist.

In the case of musculoskeletal injuries, such as back and wrist injuries, the toxic agent that an ergonomics specialist seeks to minimize is produced by the body itself. In cumulative trauma disorders the muscles are often the culprits in the development of injuries. As muscles contract, they place forces on the joints and joint or soft tissue. Most workplace musculoskeletal injuries are the result of repetitive, forceful contraction of muscles in response to physical workplace requirements. The cumulative effect may be damage to the joint or soft tissue. Most toxic exposure management involves monitoring the toxic exposure to the worker and comparing it to a predetermined safe level. In the case of musculoskeletal injury, the toxic exposure is produced by the activities of the body itself under specific workplace conditions and requirements. Monitoring and measuring the internal body joint forces that cause this toxic exposure requires either the use of bio-instrumentation or bio-mechancial models to simulate body function and response. There are a few noninvasive techniques available to measure body function during activity. As mentioned in chapter 2, EMG assessments can be very useful in determining the extent of muscle activity required to perform a specific task.

As with developing and designing products for the right fit, *muscles talk, it pays to listen,* applies equally to cumulative injuries in the workplace. The two basic questions to ask concerning muscle activity are:

1. What percent of an individual's maximum voluntary muscle capacity is needed to perform the task?

2. Does task performance produce significant fatigue?

The answer to the first question is far easier to obtain and interpret using surface measurements and EMG recorders. The acceptable percentage of maximum voluntary contraction (%MVC) is usually determined on a case-by-case basis by comparing muscle responses with comfort or musculoskeletal questionnaire responses. Answering the second question requires measuring the Fast Fourier Transform (FFT) of the EMG signal during a representative work cycle (for example, while performing a particular task throughout a typical duration, say one day). FFTs determine the energy transmitted in a wave-form for each of the different transmission frequencies. From this information it is possible for an ergonomic specialist to extract the relative magnitude of fatigue by measuring the mean, low frequency shift of the EMG power spectrum. As the muscle fatigues, the mean power frequency shifts lower. However, cutoff scores for muscle fatigue using this method, though suggested, have yet to be validated.

The Increase in Musculoskeletal Injuries

The current trend of an increase in musculoskeletal injuries in the workplace is likely to increase due to the following factors:

- The aging of the workforce (see Figure 7-3). As one ages, the prevalence of musculoskeletal injuries increases (B.C.H. De Zwart, et al., 1995). In the Netherlands, 1.1 workers in 1000, aged 15 to 24, and 8.0 workers in 1000, aged 45 to 64 were disabled due to musculoskeletal injuries.

- A greater number of women are entering the workforce (see Figure 7-4).

- Awareness of work-related musculoskeletal problems is increasing.

- Diagnostic tests have been improved.

- Human resources, medical, and safety personnel have been trained to report and address early signs and symptoms.

- The number of computer users in the workforce during the past twenty years has increased (this contribution may be mitigated by improved interface design, speech-to-text recognition, etc.).

- Production requirements have increased due to competitive pressures.

- Occupational health and reporting in developing nations has improved.

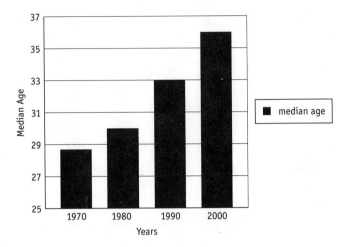

Figure 7-3. Aging of the U.S. Population

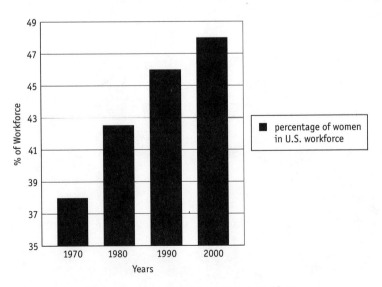

Figure 7-4. Percentage of Women in U.S. Workforce

BACK INJURIES IN THE WORKPLACE

There are many different types of cumulative musculoskeletal injuries. The rest of this chapter discusses two of these—back and wrist injuries, as well as strategies for preventing injury. It is with these kinds of injuries—through ergonomic products and workstation design—that ergonomic quality is having a beneficial impact on companies. When a company consistently focuses on objective measurement and implementation of injury prevention strategies benefits result. As Figure 7-5 shows, during the last four years the rate of cumulative trauma disorders

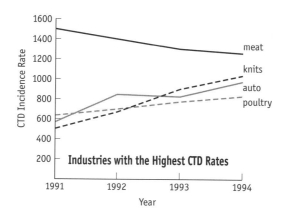

Figure 7-5. Ergonomic Success in the Meat Industry

(CTDs) has declined for the meat packing industry. By comparison, the three other industries with the highest incidence rates have been rising. In 1988, the year OSHA published its *Ergonomics Guidelines for the Meat Packing Industry,* the meat packing industry had the worst incidence rates in industry. These figures provide evidence that the employer ergonomics programs have a positive effect.

A back injury is one of the most debilitating injuries for a worker and a constant pain in the financial side for companies in terms of lost worker days, worker efficiency, medical cost, insurance premiums, litigation cost, claims management, and worker's compensation claims (between 19 and 25 percent of all worker's compensation claims are due to back injuries). Apart from headaches, low back pain is the most frequently reported cause of pain in the U.S. and the major reason for physician contact. Approximately 35 billion dollars is spent annually on back injuries in the U.S. In Sweden, Norway, and Denmark, musculoskeletal disorders cost between 3 and 5 percent of the Gross National Product (Winkel & Westgaard, 1996). The annual incidence of low back pain is 15 to 20 percent, and approximately 7 million people get back injuries each year in the U.S. About 90 percent of the population suffers a significant back injury during their lifetime. One percent of the U.S. population is chronically disabled by back symptoms. Despite improved medical care and technology, there has been little decline in back injuries.

Attacks of back pain are somewhat self-limiting and regardless of the kind of treatment used, most people feel better in about four weeks. Ninety percent feel better within six weeks. Yet the rate of recurrence for these injuries is approximately 70 to 80 percent, which means that if you injure your back today, you have a 70 percent chance of reinjuring yourself, regardless of the treatment you received, in the next 12 months. Why are the numbers so high? And is there anything companies can do to adapt and help?

Personnel Cost

It is important for management to understand the systemic causes that underlie these alarming numbers. Rather than becoming exasperated by employees' recurring back injuries, or just writing them off as an inherent business cost, management can learn about the mechanics of the disc and muscles and how they relate to force. With this understanding a company can directly alleviate many factors in the workplace that contribute to the high incidence of back problems.

One of the goals of continuous improvement is to eliminate the *wasted motion* of the worker. This approach indirectly deals with the four elements of cumulative musculoskeletal injuries (force, frequency, posture, vibration exposures). With continuous improvement programs, management and employees seek ways to improve worker performance. Among other things, this may entail changing the way a worker goes about performing a task, the tools the worker uses, and the design of the workstation. The goal here is to take the wasted motion of the worker, turn it into *actual work,* and in so doing, improve work flow. Improving the work flow enhances the value of your product. This focus on job efficiency improvement goes back to the father of scientific management, Frank Gilbreth (1868-1924), and his One Best Way to do any job. Though his scientific method was in the service of speed, he had a motto, "Work smarter, not harder," and he believed it was management's responsibility to find the simplest and easiest way to do the work (Robinson, 1991).

In an ergonomically designed work environment, the emphasis is reversed. With the ergonomics approach a company deals directly with the four elements of musculoskeletal injuries, which in turn, indirectly improve efficiency and speed. The emphasis of approach may be reversed when compared to continuous improvement, but the outcome may be far more beneficial to a company. By directly addressing and improving the safety and comfort of the worker, a company also transforms wasted motion into actual work motion, making for a healthier, happier, and "smarter" worker.

Like materials cost, personnel cost does not add value to the product. Just as a company can change the manufacturing method by using continuous improvement to eliminate personnel cost, it can likewise reduce personnel cost with an ergonomically designed workplace. Today, it is management's responsibility to go beyond continuous improvement methods and directly acknowledge and eliminate the waste in their companies that may be caused by poorly designed workplaces. Such workplaces may contribute to the high incidence of cumulative muscular injury.

The Weak Link Is the Disc

Back pain and injury are common symptoms of many diseases that affect the joints, soft tissue, and bones of the spine. Additionally, diseases of the pelvis and abdomen may also cause back pain. Back pain can be instantaneous or cumulative, depending on the magnitude of the forces placed upon the body and an individual's own susceptibility or weaknesses. Most occupationally induced back injuries are cumulative in nature. The exact cause of back pain is found in only 12 to 15 percent of the patients (Skinner, et al., 1995). Although there is much disagreement and lack of understanding regarding the pathogenesis of back injuries, most view the disc as the weak link, and the component of the spine most often damaged.

Healthy and diseased discs readily indicate the role of hydration in normal disc function. Healthy discs are filled with water, while diseased discs are dry. It is nearly impossible for a dry disc to distribute heavy loads without further damaging it, which in turn further contributes to breaking down the back's stress distribution system.

The structure of the disc makes it highly resistant to instantaneous damage. The disc is actually a water-powered, biomechanical/biochemical machine for dissipating large compressive forces into hoop stresses. This is a slow, thankless, and mostly insensate activity. As loads are applied to the vertebrae they increase the pressure of the nucleus or fluid center of the disc. The nucleus is that center portion of the spinal disc, which contains 70 to 90% water in a gelatinous form (see Figure 7-6).

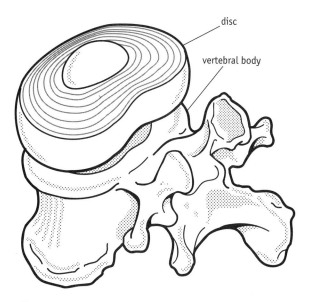

Figure 7-6. Illustration of Vertebral Body and Intervertebral Disc

The water content not only distributes vertebral stress, but also accounts for the loss in height one experiences throughout the day, and in the long run, throughout a person's life. In the morning, you are four to nine millimeters taller than in the evening. While some think back injuries are related to poor management and mechanics on the part of the person, a more correct reason is that there are cumulative forces on the disc that squeeze out a portion of the fluid when you bear (carry) loads. This fluid is then replenished during rest, as the disc reabsorbs water when spinal loads are reduced.

When loads press on the nucleus of the disc, the disc seeks to redistribute the pressure. A diseased disc subjected to loads compresses or flattens more than a healthy disc (see Figure 7-7). For a 100 kilogram load, a diseased disc flattens 2.0 millimeters while a healthy disc flattens only 1.4 millimeters.

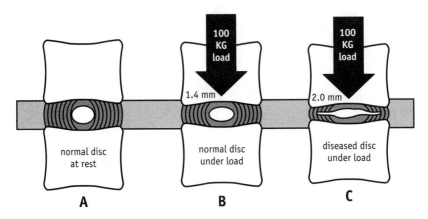

Figure 7-7. Effects of Different Loads on Disc Flattening

The central portion or nucleus of the disc is surrounded by annular fibers, like a bias belted automobile tire. Approximately 90 layers of these collagen-based fibers (the same stuff that fingernails are made of) are laid down in alternating orientations like plywood. Each successive layer has approximately a 30 degree orientation to the endplate of the disc (see Figure 7-8).

This makes for one very tough container for the nucleus. Pressures building up in the nucleus cause a ballooning or stretching of the fibers of the annulus, creating what are known as hoop stresses. For the same reason that we place hoops around barrels of pickles or wine to counteract the ballooning tendency of the barrel when they are stacked, annular fibers are nature's spinal hoops for absorbing the compressive loads placed on the discs.

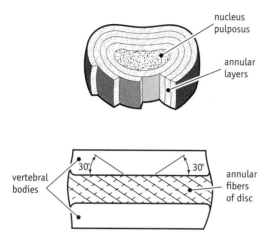

Figure 7-8. Fiber Structure in the Disc for Added Strength

Anatomy of Pain and Injury to the Spine

There is much argument about the actual body mechanism that causes pain and injury to the spine. Many say discs; others spinal muscles, ligaments, facet joints, abdominal muscles, and even the shape of the spine itself, as in the case of scoliosis (spinal curvature). This seems of little consequence in the final analysis. All of the aforementioned components of the spine work together to achieve the common goal: the movement, positioning, and generation of force for our body in space. The bones provide the compressive strength, the facet joints control our motions, the abdominal and back muscles generate the force and also control our motion, the ligaments distribute the forces over larger areas so as not to cause a concentration of force or stress and also help define the motion. Indeed, some of the long spinal ligaments (the posterior longitudinal ligament) seem to grow out of the disc itself, in an effort to spread the effective flexibility of the disc over the larger surface of the vertebrae.

The spine is a complete, beautifully designed system for managing forces placed on the body, and can usually perform its function for the duration of a person's lifetime. It is not the design of the spine that is usually at fault in manufacturing injuries, but rather the factors that account for cumulative trauma. When this cumulative trauma finally produces a spinal injury, the initial pain a person feels is also a measurement of the degree of system dysfunction and damage.

In the early stages of a spinal injury the muscles go into a spasm and, like a corset, help protect the underlying soft tissue from further damage by preventing additional body movement. Muscles have two primary functions—to move and moor the body in space. But muscles in spasm are no longer available to produce movement as either a protagonist or antagonist to body motion. This has the undesirable consequence of less body control during motion as well as greater force on the facet joints. Furthermore, muscles that have been subjected to spasms are more susceptible to future spasms with little provocation. This is almost like an allergic response, far surpassing the magnitude of the allergen. When muscles respond this way, they are described as being twitchy. This frequent twitching of the muscle has, in addition to producing pain and limiting movement, the negative consequence of placing great force on the disc unnecessarily, and potentially further damaging the annular fibers. This is why if a worker has back spasms, it is best that they immediately cease what they are doing and rest. They should not in any form or fashion work through the pain, or twitching. This is by no means the definitive pathogenesis of low back pain, but it is a plausible description of the mechanical mechanisms for commonly reported pain and injury to the spine.

Damage to the spine, as well as the process of healing, is complicated by the fact that the disc receives no direct blood supply (bradytrophic) after adolescence. As a result, the disc obtains nutrients and gets rid of the waste products of metabolism by exchanging fluids through the

porous, cartilaginous endplates. As a result of the indirect nutrient supply, the disc produces new cells slowly. Once a person damages a disc it
may take months or years for the body to repair the torn annular fibers.
It is also important to note that well before the damaged disc is fully
repaired, the pain usually subsides. This false sense of well-being occurs
because the outer layers of the annulus have healed so the nerve root is
no longer being pressed or pinched by the nucleus. However, many layers of the annular material may still be damaged, and the repairs may
have produced scar tissue with significantly less flexibility. All of this
points back to the potential for reinjury and explains to some degree
why the reinjury rate is 70 percent. People with spinal injuries simply
return too quickly to normal life and work, compromising a system that
has not had sufficient time to heal. Though there is no pain, people need
to take their time and gradually and incrementally return to their normal life. It is especially important to avoid repetitive movements or
heavy loads that may aggravate the spine.

For any type of musculoskeletal injury, especially for spinal injuries,
management should have a program in place to monitor and assist the
worker in the long-term healing process. Simply reducing the present
load or even training the worker to perform a less strenuous, repetitive
task, would go a long way to getting back a healthy productive worker.

Possible Causes of Back Injury

A review of back injuries in 26 states by the U.S. Department of
Labor showed the following characteristics:

- The majority of movements at the time of injury were
  bending and twisting.
- The average duration an object was held at the time of
  injury was less than one minute.

- Of those who reported back injury, 30 percent lift objects over 100 times per day.

- The weight range of objects lifted at the time of injury was 40 to 100 pounds in 70 percent of the cases and over 100 pounds in 30 percent of the cases.

- The distance that the load was carried in 80 percent of the back injury cases was less than five feet.

- The position of the load at the point of injury was on the floor in 50 percent of the cases.

- Thirty-five percent of the workers felt that the loads that they lifted were too heavy.

- Approximately 50 percent of the workers who reported injuries had previous back injury.

- The position of the back at the time of injury was fully or partially flexed in 83 percent of the cases.

Although many disagree on how back injuries develop, there is good agreement as to the basic stressors that contribute to the development of back injuries. Three of the four elements that cause cumulative musculoskeletal injuries—cumulative force, frequency, and posture—relate directly to back injuries. The forth element, vibration, has a greater impact on upper extremity injuries.

Force. This becomes a factor when loads are placed on the joints while holding something or moving the body. For example, while holding a box at waist level in front of the body, the force placed on the lower lumbar spinal disc (L4-L5) may be equal to ten times the load held in the hands.

It has been known for more than 20 years that lumbo-sacral, spinal compressive forces (L5 through S1) are related to the incidence of low back pain. In fact, the incidence of low back pain is almost ten times as great when the forces on the spine range from 250 to 650 kilograms (see Figure 7-9).

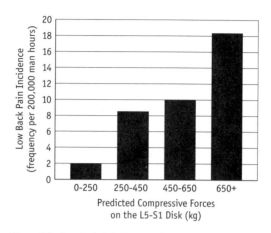

Figure 7-9. Low Back Pain Versus Spinal Compressive Forces

In general, as the compressive forces on the spine increase, so do the back injuries. When cumulative force on the spine is factored in, even lesser forces may eventually cause a back injury. Companies can consider this fundamental fact as reason enough to rationalize a control strategy for musculoskeletal injuries to the spine.

There is currently a mechanism for companies to monitor spinal forces. The National Institute of Occupational Safety and Health (NIOSH) recommends that spinal forces be kept below approximately 3400 Newtons, as this level seems to protect the majority of workers who perform lifting and associated tasks. A Newton is approximately equal to the weight of a small English apple (0.22 lbs.). These loads sound heavy, but are, in fact, amplified by the high muscle forces within the body needed to stabilize the spine.

Frequency. The frequency with which a worker performs a task becomes an important factor when you consider the rate at which repetitive movement occurs. For example, it is important to know the number of times a worker has to make the same movement on an assembly line.

Working postures. Specifically, working postures relate to the position in which the body is held while performing a task. Working postures greatly affect the loads on the spine (see Figure 7-10). Sitting and leaning forward increase spinal compressive forces by 90 percent when compared with standing. This information was acquired by inserting a needle into the intravertebral discs of Swedish medical students. The tip of the needle contained a small pressure transducer. This technique is known as intravital discometry and is largely responsible for our understanding of spinal forces *in vivo*.

It is interesting to note that sitting increases spinal loads. As you sit

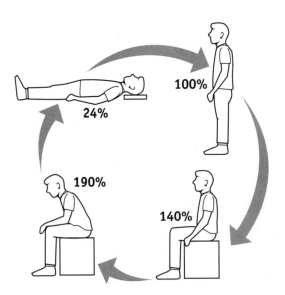

Figure 7-10. Disc Pressure as a Function of Body Position

on the bones at the base of the pelvis (ischial tuberosities) the pelvis rotates backwards, flattening the spine by about 38 degrees. Depending on what your low back curve (lordosis) was while standing, your back when you are seated may become flat or convexly curved (kyphotic) (see Figure 7-11). Also, if you apply loads to your feet while seated, increased forces on the disc will result. This kinetic chain occurs as you extend the lower leg and stretch the hamstring muscle. The pelvis rotates (pulls it forward from the bottom), which in turn flattens the spine further, increasing disc pressure. This is a good reason to use cruise control on long trips, so as to minimize cumulative spinal forces.

The basic implication of all of this for management is that job responsibilities and environments should be designed in such a way that postures vary between sitting and standing. This changes the pressure on the spine and promotes the exchange of fluids in the disc.

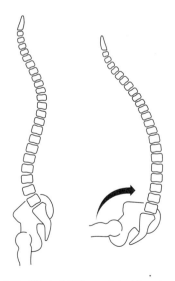

Figure 7-11. Effect of Sitting on Spinal Curvature

A summary of what ergonomics specialists know about the dose-response relationship between workplace exposures and the development of back injuries, follows:

WHAT CONSTITUTES ACCEPTABLE SPINAL FORCE EXPOSURE?

- <3400 Newtons of compressive force on L5/S1
  (Putz-Anderson, Waters and Garg, 1993)

- Lateral trunk velocity <42 deg/sec or twisting <8 deg/sec when combined with trunk flexion, movement, and frequent lift rates
  (Marris, et al 1995)

- Frequency of lifting <120 lifts/hour
  (Marris, et al 1995)

- Psychophysical—loads less than 75% of female workers maximum acceptable weight of lift, and 99% of male workers maximum acceptable weight of lift

Measure and Control

The key concept for management in decreasing stressful loads on a worker's back is that you can only manage what you can measure. At the beginning of this century one of the major health problems facing U.S. industry was occupationally-induced deafness. Two developments helped reduce this problem of epidemic proportions to a minor, mainte-nance-oriented, safety program: the development of the sound-level meter and the development of cutoff scores for determining if recorded levels of exposure were safe or acceptable—measure and control.

In the case of back injuries in the workplace, the meter is a comput-er-based, biomechanical model, which, in the case of force exposure to the spine, allows for an estimation. The cutoff scores begin with the NIOSH recommended cutoff of 3400 Newtons. This is of course some-what primitive, but is a good start and a correct method with which to measure and control the very great manufacturing cost resulting from back injuries.

Science has always predicted the future and hypothesized what we can do about it. The science of biomechanics allows us to predict whether or not an individual will get a back injury. Since the control of spinal compressive forces leads to the reduction in low back injuries, the challenge for management is to measure and reduce these forces. And workplace ergonomics is one of the few cost-effective avenues available to help companies in this regard.

WRIST INJURIES IN THE WORKPLACE

Though back pain is the largest cause of pain in the U.S. and the major reason for physician contact, the current trend for upper extremity musculoskeletal injuries (wrist, hands, elbows, shoulders) is increasing. Although there is no definitive answer to why this is so, I don't believe a true epidemic has been uncovered. The most significant change in workplace exposure to the upper extremity, since 1970, has been the introduction of computers in the workplace. In 1978, approximately 200,000 individuals operated computers in the U.S. By 1990, this number had increased to 30 million. Currently, more than 50 million computers are in use in business in the United States. Most of these jobs involve office work environments and consist of clerical, secretarial, data entry and professional/computer-intensive vocations, such as accounting and programming. However, most of the musculoskeletal injuries since 1970 are from the industrial/manufacturing sector where the upper extremity is engaged in manufacturing, inspection, and packaging operations. Therefore the approximately 10 percent increases, both in the median age of the working population and percent of women in the workforce, do not explain the growth in upper extremity cumulative trauma disorders.

In 1986, I conducted a study for the Attorney General of the Commonwealth of Australia to compare the occurrence of cumulative trauma disorders in Australian and U.S. employees with similar levels of physical work exposure. What we found was that for a select industry, the Australian workers reported up to fifteen times the incidence of cumulative trauma disorders when compared with a similar demographic group of U.S. workers in a similar workplace task. As a side issue, many other independent studies were undertaken to evaluate and compare the water, nutritional uptake, psycho-social, and cultural differences between the two countries. Why were the reported incidence rates so different?

Our ergonomic team viewed the problem as one of evaluating cause and effect. From a biomechanical perspective, as you increase the physical exposure you increase the potential for developing a cumulative trauma disorder. If the physical exposures are similar, as they were between the U.S. and Australian workers, and the incidence rates are very different, the problem lies outside the dose-response relationship. This led us to believe that the Australian injury classification system was causing the high incidence rates.

At the time, in Australia, there was a common grab-bag diagnosis called RSI (Repetitive Strain Injury). As the criteria for having an RSI was not firmly established or agreed upon, almost any individual with pain and discomfort of the upper extremity, who happened to be performing repetitive tasks in a job, could be diagnosed as having RSI. There is a difference, however, between pain, discomfort, and injury/disease. On the same scale, discomfort would be at one end, pain in the middle, and injury/disease on the other end, but injury/disease requires differential diagnostic criteria. The reason Australian workers reported up to fifteen times the incidence of cumulative trauma disorders when compared to U.S. workers was that the Australian Government reported, not the incidence of injury/disease, but rather the incidence of something between discomfort/pain and injury/disease.

This kind of scale classification system really only makes sense for developing a model of cumulative mechanical exposure that produces these types of injuries. This is why questionnaires inquiring about pain and discomfort are useful in the evaluation of early responses to work-place exposures. A model of cumulative mechanical exposures tells us that it would be impossible to get cumulative trauma injury, for example, to the wrist, without having repeated episodes of pain and discomfort.

The growth of the reported incidents of cumulative trauma disorders (CTDs) in the U.S. may reflect a similar reporting problem. The difference is that the work-relatedness of what was accepted as an inevitable by-product of work or aging is now associated with specific workplace exposures and compensation issues (see Figure 7-10). For example, surveys of people who work at computers all day show that it is not uncommon to find that 70 to 80 percent report pain and discomfort. In one large study that we performed for a U.S. government agency, only 0.5 percent of the population actually had CTDs when medically evaluated with an objective diagnostic criteria. The difference between 0.5 percent and 70 to 80 percent is large and subject to the quality, rigor, and uniformity of the diagnostic criteria.

With improved, yet imperfect, understanding of the work-related-ness of cumulative trauma injuries that ergonomics shows us, we may be seeing, for the first time, something close to the true incidence rates. If this is true, future increases due to misclassification and ignorance with respect to work-relatedness should not significantly change the incidence numbers. We are left, therefore, to consider the other factors that may affect the growth in CTD rates.

Like back injuries, wrist injuries can result from exposure to cumulative force, frequency, posture, and vibration. Simplistic as it may sound, the majority of damaging cumulative trauma exposures occur when one or more of these four elements are combined with insufficient rest (see Figure 7-12). Regardless of the way we interpret diagnostic criteria and/or the worker's desire for compensation, we still see a large number of complaints of pain and discomfort with the hand and wrist. Why?

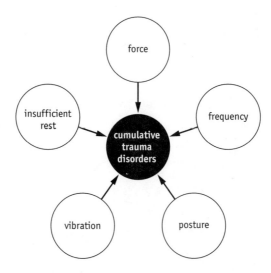

Figure 7-12. Stressors That Contribute to the Development of Cumulative Trauma Disorders

The Mechanics of the Hand and Wrist

The body is both protean and flexible and is well-suited to perform a diverse number of activities. A basic concept in overuse syndromes, such as carpal tunnel syndrome and low back pain, is that what otherwise would be a tolerable level of stress is transformed into a toxic exposure by the cumulative force of highly repetitive product use or work methods. The body usually doesn't tolerate this well, especially if the rate of exposure from the work is greater than the healing or resting time the body requires for a particular injury or activity.

Frequency. Repeated activities are most prevalent in the operations of assembly, inspection, manufacturing, and data-entry tasks. The rapid, repeated performance of these tasks, especially when wrist accelerations exceed 800 deg/sec**≤, causes both friction and pressure to increase in the carpal canal. This occurs because the hand is extremely light in weight. One important characteristic of a great tool is a high strength-to-weight ratio. Think of the difficulty a surgeon would have performing an incision with a 15 pound scalpel. To optimize control, a positioning tool should have as little mass as possible.

Force. Muscles are relatively heavy. A typical pair of hands weighs 2.6 pounds (1.18 kilograms), which represents only 1.7 percent of body weight. Yet the hands are strong, with average grasping strength between 50 and 60 pounds. The muscles that generate these forces are largely located on the forearms. Using a pulley and rope system (carpal canal and wrist tendons), these forearm muscle forces are transmitted to the hands (see Figure 7-13).

This high strength-to-weight ratio of the hands allows them to be wonderful tools when empowered with neuromuscular control. When high hand forces are needed to move and moor the hand and fingers, the forearm flexor and extensor muscles are recruited. They in turn contract, pulling on the flexor and extensor tendons that pass through

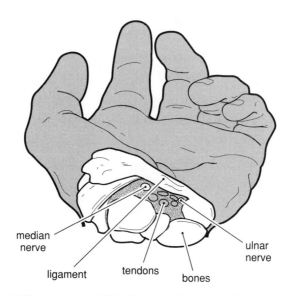

median
nerve

ulnar
nerve

ligament   tendons   bones

Figure 7-13. Cross-section of Wrist Showing Median Nerve and Finger Tendons

the carpal canal. Additionally, the intrinsic muscles help smooth out the changes in the shape of the hand (see Figure 7-14), allowing it to form around a wide variety of shapes, yet still apply significant force.

Median nerve pressure. As the hand exerts force or changes from the neutral position, carpal canal pressure and friction both increase. This increase in pressure is probably responsible for increased irritation to the median nerve, which is the definition of carpal tunnel syndrome. The median nerve gives life to the first three and a half fingers of the hand, beginning with the thumb. This nerve provides the main conduit between the brain and the hand. Stressors such as strong forces, vibration, awkward posture (a poor mooring position), or cold temperatures, may cause the nerve and/or its blood supply to become occluded, much as would happen if you were to squeeze a garden hose. One aspect of increased carpal canal pressure is decreased nerve response. Typically, people with irritation to the median nerve require a longer period of time

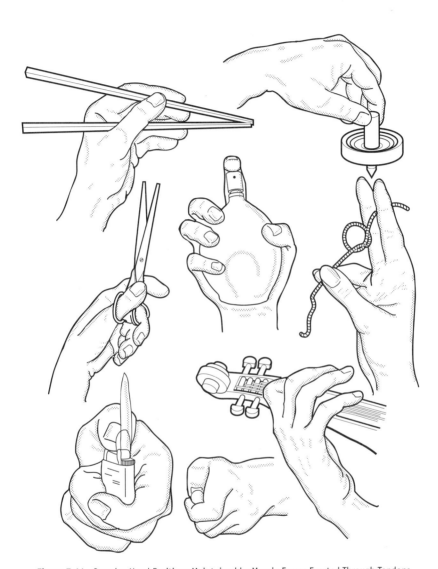

Figure 7-14. Complex Hand Positions Maintained by Muscle Forces Exerted Through Tendons

for the nerve to conduct current through the wrist. One way to determine if a worker is suffering from increased carpal canal pressure is to measure the time it takes for the nerve to conduct electricity through the wrist. Median nerve conduction velocity tests are routinely performed as part of the diagnostic evaluation for carpal tunnel syndrome.

Vibration. Vibration is also a factor in upper extremity cumulative injuries. These types of injuries result from the oscillations produced from moving parts within tools and equipment. As an example, the use of chain saws by forest workers may impart significant vibration into the hands and fingers. Over time, this may result in the development of White Finger Syndrome due to reduced blood supply to the fingers.

After back injuries, wrist injuries are responsible for more lost work time in the United States than any other occupational illness. Companies can prepare for and deal with these increasing injuries by instructing those responsible for the design of the workplace tasks to minimize the cumulative force exposures to the body that can contribute to upper extremity cumulative trauma disorders.

Injury Prevention Tools for the Wrist

The difference between illness and injury is measured by the time frame in which the problem occurs. The Occupational Health and Safety Administration historically has classified injuries as occurring instantaneously, while illnesses were thought to develop over time. In the case of back and wrist injuries, the distinction is meaningless. These injuries almost always occur over time. Many of OSHA's surveillance forms are therefore less useful then they could be, for example, accident investigation forms that ask the question, What posture were you in at the time of injury? In the case of musculoskeletal injuries, where thousands or millions of cycles of exposure are responsible for developing the injury, such questions are too simplistic to be of value.

Likewise, ergonomists, as a group, have fallen short by not quantifying the dose-response relationship associated with the development of

WHAT CONSTITUTES ACCEPTABLE WORKPLACE WRIST EXPOSURES?

• Wrist acceleration <820deg/sec**2
(Marras 1991, 1995)

• Median nerve pressure <30 mm Hg
(Rydevik et al. 1981, Lundbord 1977, 1982)

• Forces on the hand <4.5 kg (10 lb.)
(Silverstein et al. 1987)

• Repetition-cycle time ≥30 sec
(Lifshitz and Armstrong 1986)

cumulative trauma disorders. The profession must develop a tool that allows the practitioner to measure exposures and compare these exposures to cut-off scores that have been validated to indicate that discomfort, pain, or likely injury will result if the activity is continued unabated. This is not so difficult as it sounds, yet until it is done, real progress in the management-prevention of cumulative trauma disorders to the upper extremity will be hampered. As a small step in this direction I have developed a wrist stress monitor to measure muscle force, 3-D wrist position, wrist velocity, frequency of wrist motions and duration of exposure. The monitor puts a number on wrist stress between 1 and 100, indicating the level of exposure. The validation of this device with specific injury and discomfort cut-off levels now needs to be performed.

Another tool that managers can use was developed by Dr. Marras, who determined acceleration signatures of wrist motion, especially during flexion and extension. This test can be very telling in determining the propensity for workers to develop a cumulative wrist injury. Specifically, Dr. Marris indicates that wrist accelerations during flexion and extension that average 820 deg/sec2 or more, are eight times more likely to be associated with a CTD when compared with wrist accelerations averaging 490 deg/sec2. It might be easy to develop a device where wrist accelerations are displayed with indicated color zones (see Figure 7-15), although presently such a device does not exist.

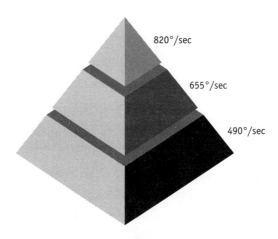

820°/sec

655°/sec

490°/sec

Figure 7-15. Wrist Safety Pyramid

As the pyramid narrows, so does the margin of safety. This device (a dosimeter) could indicate wrist acceleration as green (0 to 490 deg/sec2), yellow (655 deg/sec2), and red (7820 deg/sec2). The result could serve as a wrist safety pyramid. Similar pyramids could be used to indicate stressful exposures to the back, and so on. The caveat is, however, that no one measurement of stress is likely to be able to warn all potential users of wrist injury.

Numerous researchers have found that in addition to wrist accelerations, the following all play a role in wrist injuries (Helander):

- hand flexion

- extension

- ulnar deviation

- radial deviation

- quantity of motions

- vibration

- duration of exposure

Then there are the broader factors that contribute to wrist injuries to consider (these can also affect potential back injuries). Such factors are:

- pre-existing conditions

- experience

- leisure activities

- poor work methods

One could say that all of these factors are inextricably interwoven into a unique injury potential. The ability to identify and measure one specific type of toxic physical exposure would be a good starting point for a comprehensive exposure control program. However, managers must take another tack, as no effective assessment device exists for the prevention of wrist injuries. Though one can easily imagine an acceleration monitor for the wrist, currently, the best one can do is minimize discomfort, a known precursor to injury. Management can achieve this by minimizing wrist deviations, wrist forces, wrist vibration, and cold exposures during work.

A Case in Point

A major producer of glass automobile windshields in North America had a history of wrist injuries in the department responsible for trimming the plastic used to fuse adjacent sheets of glass in the manufacture of safety glass. They called in a workplace ergonomics specialist to evaluate both the physical production requirements and the wrist stressors that result from trimming the plastic with a razor-sharp, sheet-rock knife. The ergonomist measured wrist postures and repetitions by having the workers wear thin, instrumented gloves that measured 3-D movements of the wrist. Analysis of the data indicated that complaints of wrist discomfort and reported injury were likely due to the combination of ulnar deviation of the wrist (side bending towards the small finger) and flexion produced with each cutting stroke. The ergonomist designed a new knife handle that accommodated the same blades currently used. This new handle, however, had a custom-tailored curve to minimize wrist deviation. Also, the new knife handle had a larger surface area that allowed users to hold the knife with less force. The ergonomics consultant subcontracted the manufacturing of a small batch of these test handles out of high-density, urethane foam. This produced a handle that would bend slightly under large forces, rather than transmit all of the force to the wrist. After also improving blade replacement, the newly designed tools were well accepted. The result was a marked reduction in pain and discomfort during trimming operations.

Using Questionnaires

Questionnaires can be very helpful to the manager evaluating the potential for wrist injuries. Table 7-1 shows a reprint of a musculoskeletal questionnaire (Kuorinka and Forcier, 1995) that is a good example of an inexpensive, preliminary surveillance tool with which to determine whether a wrist injury problem is likely to develop.

In addition, a risk-factor checklist can be very useful to management for identifying workplace stressors (see Table 7-2).

Dr. Helander presents a concise set of guidelines much like previous lists presented by one of the founders of workplace ergonomics, Dr. Tichauer (see Figure 7-16).

There may be some good news on the horizon for many organizations. Though it may not affect wrist problems in manufacturing, computer users are likely see significant relief of wrist problems with the introduction of voice-to-text programs. While these programs are in their first or second generation currently, two or three years from now the 200MHz processor, combined with improved speech recognition, should enable many data entry persons to alternate between audible and keyed input to control workload and wrist stress. Further, inexpensive optical character recognition software will further reduce the necessity for manual analog-to-digital conversion (data entry). The result should be fewer wrist injuries worldwide.

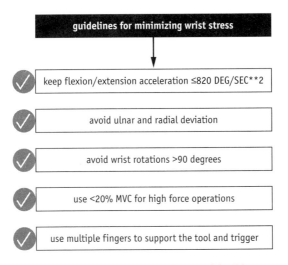

Figure 7-16. Guidelines for Reducing CTD of the Wrist

Table 7-1. Musculoskeletal Questionnaire (1 of 3)

Name:

Date:

Gender:

Shift:

Job:

Front   Back

Time on this job:

<3 months	3 months—1 year
>1 year to 5 years	>5 years to 10 years
>10 years	

How often are you mentally exhausted
after work?

| Never | Seldom |
| Often | Always |

Have you ever had pain or discomfort during
the last year that you believed to be related
to your work?

| Yes | No |

p–pain   b–burning
nt–numbness/tingling
pnt–pain/numbness/tingling
a–ache   sw–swelling
st–stiffness   o–other
If the answer is yes, shade in the
areas on the drawings above which
bother you the most.
For each area you shade in label
what kind of discomfort you have
experienced.

Table 7-1. Musculoskeletal Questionnaire (2 of 3)

	Neck	Shoulder	Elbow/ Forearm	Hand/ Wrist	Fingers
1. Which side bothers you?	Left Right Both	Left Right Both	Left Right Both	Left Right Both	Left Right Both
2. When did you first notice this problem?	Left Right Both	Left Right Both	Left Right Both	Left Right Both	Left Right Both
3. How long does the problem usually last?	A D B E C F	A D B E C F	A D B E C F	A D B E C F	A D B E C F
4. How many separate times have you had this problem?	A D B E C F	A D B E C F	A D B E C F	A D B E C F	A D B E C F
5. What do you think caused the problem?					
6. Problem in the last 7 days?	Yes No	Yes No	Yes No	Yes No	Yes No
7. According to the scale of 0–5, how would you rate the problem now?	Rating	Rating	Rating	Rating	Rating
8. Have you had medical treatment for this problem?	Yes No	Yes No	Yes No	Yes No	Yes No
9. Days of work lost in the last year due to this problem?	____days	____days	____days	____days	____days
10. Days of light or restricted duty in the last year due to this problem?	____days	____days	____days	____days	____days
11. Have you changed jobs because of this problem?	Yes No	Yes No	Yes No	Yes No	Yes No
12. Please comment on what you think would improve your symptoms.					

| **Key for Question 3** | A <1 hour
B 1 hour–24 hours
C >24 Hours–1 week
D >1 week–1 month
E >1 month–6 months
F >6 months | **Key for Question 4** | A Constant
B Daily
C Once a week
D Once a month
E Every 2–3 months
F More than 6 months | **Key for Question 7** | 0 No discomfort
5 Unbearable discomfort |

Table 7-1. Musculoskeletal Questionnaire (3 of 3)

	Upper Back	Low Back	Thigh/ Knee	Lower Leg	Ankle/ Foot
1. Which side bothers you?	Left Right Both	Left Right Both	Left Right Both	Left Right Both	Left Right Both
2. When did you first notice this problem?	Left Right Both	Left Right Both	Left Right Both	Left Right Both	Left Right Both
3. How long does the problem usually last?	A D B E C F	A D B E C F	A D B E C F	A D B E C F	A D B E C F
4. How many separate times have you had this problem?	A D B E C F	A D B E C F	A D B E C F	A D B E C F	A D B E C F
5. What do you think caused the problem?					
6. Problem in the last 7 days?	Yes No	Yes No	Yes No	Yes No	Yes No
7. According to the scale of 0–5, how would you rate the problem now?	Rating	Rating	Rating	Rating	Rating
8. Have you had medical treatment for this problem?	Yes No	Yes No	Yes No	Yes No	Yes No
9. Days of work lost in the last year due to this problem?	____days	____days	____days	____days	____days
10. Days of light or restricted duty in the last year due to this problem?	____days	____days	____days	____days	____days
11. Have you changed jobs because of this problem?	Yes No	Yes No	Yes No	Yes No	Yes No
12. Please comment on what you think would improve your symptoms.					

Key for Question 3		Key for Question 4		Key for Question 7	
A	<1 hour	A	Constant	0	No discomfort
B	1 hour–24 hours	B	Daily	5	Unbearable discomfort
C	>24 Hours–1 week	C	Once a week		
D	>1 week–1 month	D	Once a month		
E	>1 month–6 months	E	Every 2–3 months		
F	>6 months	F	More than 6 months		

Table 7-2. Upper Extremity Cumulative Trauma Disorder Checklist

Risk Factors	Yes	No
Physical Stress		
Can the job be done without hand/wrist contact with sharp edges?		
Is the tool operating without vibration?		
Are the worker's hands exposed to temperatures > 21 deg C?		
Can the job be done without wearing gloves?		
Force		
Does the job require exerting less than 4.5 kg of force?		
Can the job be done without using a finger pinch grip?		
Posture		
Can the job be done without > 10 degrees of flexion/extension of the wrist?		
Can the job be done without > 10 degrees of ulnar/radial deviation of the wrist?		
Can the worker alternate between seated and standing postures?		
Can the job be done without a clothes wringing motion?		
Repetitiveness		
Is the cycle time longer than 30 seconds?		
Motion		
Is the flexion/extension acceleration >490 deg/sec **2?		
Workstation		
Can the height and orientation of the work surface be adjusted?		
Can the location of the tool be easily adjusted?		
Tool Characteristics		
Is the weight of the tool below 4kg?		
Is the tool suspended overhead?		
Is the tool easy to hold?		
Are there sharp ridges on the tool?		
Is the center-of-mass of the tool located approximately at the center of the hand?		
An answer of yes indicates the presence of a musculoskeletal stressor.		

ADMINISTRATIVE AND ENGINEERING CONTROLS

Ergonomics would have little value to the manager if from its precepts, extensive knowledge base, and experience, it could not generalize a set of rules for the prevention of workplace injuries. After all, ergonomics is the science that seeks to adapt work or working conditions to fit the worker. In addition to the use of biomechanics and product design, we can consider two classes of controls: administrative and engineering. These controls further break down into five practical and traditional categories as follows:

1. Personal protective equipment

2. Training

3. Preplacement screening

4. Workplace assessments

5. Workplace and tool modifications

By definition, to be considered successful, a musculoskeletal intervention strategy must show either a decrease in the cumulative stressors applied to the body or a decrease in the occurrence of injuries that result from those stressors. In the case of back injuries, for example, the former is somewhat practical to achieve, the latter is nearly impossible. Why? The large number of confounding variables that contribute to back injuries obscure the small, yet potentially meaningful, changes in incidence rates.

Companies cannot predict who will get a back injury based on age, gender, smoking history, weight, X-ray findings, family history, or occupation. Yet, it is not unreasonable to assume that a successful management-prevention strategy for injuries could reduce a cumulative force exposure to the body by 2 percent. Someone who lifts a 40-pound load 200 times per day, with each lift placing 3200 Newtons on the spine, multiplied by 5 seconds, has a total force exposure of 3.2 million Newtons per day, or 800 million Newtons per year. A 2-percent reduction would mean 16 million fewer Newtons on the spine per year. Remembering that a Newton weighs about as much as a small English apple (about 0.22 pounds), the result is a large savings in potentially toxic spinal exposures.

Would a company able to achieve such an exposure reduction show a concomitant reduction in back injury rates? Probably not, due to the confounding variables. When 70 to 80 percent of a population have a back problem sometime in their lives, even a successful musculoskeletal intervention strategy may not change the number of people who get the injury, but rather might delay its onset by a decade or reduce its severity, convalescing time, and recurrence rate. Success is relative, but certainly these kinds of improvements can translate into cost savings. Still, it would be better for a company to focus on all of the available methods for reducing the risk factors that contribute to back injuries, than to rely on any one intervention method. The rest of this chapter discusses the five major administrative and engineering controls mentioned above.

Personal Protective Equipment

When one looks at the primary prevention strategies for injuries that have identifiable toxic exposures and dose-response relationships, one thought comes to mind: *Control exposure to the toxic agent.*

Back support. For back injuries, the toxic exposure is cumulative spinal force. Perhaps the easiest way to control this is by transmitting some percentage of the force externally, from the torso to the pelvis, rather than internally, through the discs. This led me to develop the first prophylactic lumbar support belt, for which I received a patent in 1983. It is now a fairly ubiquitous product, worn by many individuals who perform manual materials handling, but over twelve years ago, it was a potential solution for postal workers who had to handle heavy mail sacks all day long. At the time I thought it might be possible to have personal protective equipment for protection against back injuries, just as you might have for reducing noise exposure and preventing hearing loss. I decided that by slightly stiffening the spine/torso with an exoskeletal support we could potentially achieve the following:

- Reduce the velocity and acceleration of the torso during the aggregation and segregation of loads (picking up and dropping off).

- Reduce the amount of torso twisting that is permitted, as in torsion. When twisted the spine has approximately 25 percent of the strength it has during pure compression.

- Reduce the forces of the erector spinae muscle required to stabilize the spine and, therefore, reduce the cumulative spinal compression.

A potentially good idea, but did it work? It was fairly obvious from the outset that engineering modifying postal workplaces would have only limited value and negative cost-benefit for a job with as many locations as there are street corners in the U.S. My initial study in 1983, however, indicated that, indeed, mail handlers demonstrated slightly reduced spinal compression force when lifting mail sacks freestyle with the prophylactic lumbar support belt. This was measured by recording the EMG signals from the back muscles. There was also a negative con-sequence—the forced vital capacity (the ability to force air out of the lungs) was reduced comparable to bending forward 45 degrees.

Similar results were recently reported (Udo, H., et al, 1995) after comparing 30 individuals who wore a flexible back belt for six months compared with 30 individuals who wore no belt. EMG activity, pain, and discomfort were all reduced. Another report (Magnusson, M., et al, 1996) confirms that a back support has a positive biomechanical effect.

Though approximately 100 million dollars worth of these belts are sold every year in the U.S., NIOSH recently took the position that back belts are not recommended as personal protective equipment. They may give an employee a false sense of security, potentially contribute to atrophy of the back muscles, and discourage an employer from performing ergonomic workplace engineering modifications. While there is some truth to these claims, this is a good example of how a little knowledge on the part of NIOSH can be a dangerous thing.

Having performed workplace ergonomic programs for many Fortune 500 companies, it is clear that many more workplaces are *not* amenable to reengineering, compared with those that are, for example, hospitals, retail establishments, delivery businesses, other service businesses, and outside distribution. As to NIOSH's concerns about atrophy of the back muscles, this is unlikely to occur because the reduction in spinal compressive force is quite small. Furthermore, people wear the belt for only part of the day. Even if an individual wears a belt for eight hours continuously, the remainder of the waking day would be unbelted. Rather than giving an employee a false sense of security, wearing a back belt could remind the individual to practice better lifting techniques.

Additionally, belts may reduce cumulative spinal force exposures by approximately 2 percent. Ask any weightlifter why they wear a belt and the answer is that it's slightly easier to lift the load. Yet, several recent studies that compared belt wearers with non-belt wearers concluded that back belts are not effective, due a to lack of significant relationship between perceived lifting limits and perceptual differences in strength.

Wrist supports. Using a similar rationale for controlling the exposure to the toxic agent, I developed the first prophylactic wrist supports used by industry (1982). The idea again was to minimize the unwanted motions, especially excessive flexion, extensions, ulnar, and radial deviations of the wrist. These exoskeletal supports did just that, but they also, unfortunately, severely reduced the range of motion of the wrist. Others have since improved upon the original design with lighter, more streamlined versions of wrist supports.

The caution against using wrist supports extends beyond that associated with back supports, and has greater merit. Following studies on carpal tunnel syndrome by Dr. Gelberman, who inserted wick catheters in the wrists of patients with carpal tunnel syndrome, we have learned that flexion and extension of the healthy wrist can increase carpal canal pressure and irritation to the median nerve 15 to 30 times more than when the wrist is held relatively straight with the forearm. So any support that minimizes the ability of the wrist to bend is only of value if the wrist is not forced to bend anyway under the added resistance of the support. This means that if you wear a wrist support and bend your wrist 60 degrees while performing a task, the carpal canal pressure will include the force from flexion plus the force you had to apply to bend the support. In other words, the force on the wrist increases when wearing the wrist support. Therefore, the use of wrist supports should be limited to those tasks which can be performed with a nearly straight wrist.

In short, personal protective equipment has its place in reducing cumulative force exposures to the body, though on a limited, case-by-case basis. These equipment solutions require further improvements to the stress reduction benefit before management can use them to consistently reduce injuries. Intelligent and talking body supports most likely will be the next generation for personal protective equipment. These body supports would be equipped with microprocessor-controlled joint supports that automatically adjust the range of motion and joint stiffness according to user input or a feature such as velocity, acceleration, range of motion, force, and so on. A talking body support would simply tell the user, by way of a safety factor, when their joint forces exceed some predetermined value.

Providing Meaningful Training

Training is interesting to evaluate due to the predilection of management to embark on this type of solution for exposure control and abatement. After all, most managers have training budgets, but few have ergonomic assessment and abatement budgets. Training falls roughly into five categories:

- Questionnaires for early identification of signs and symptoms

- Mastering techniques for workplace assessment

- Postural technique training

- Warm-up exercise programs

- Biofeedback training for stress reduction

In my experience with corporate training programs, training is a valuable adjunct for providing cohesion for a workplace injury prevention program. On the other hand, for outright injury prevention, management needs to focus on minimizing the stress of toxic exposures. Even the best ergonomic training program will rarely, if ever, achieve injury prevention without addressing this issue.

Questionnaires. As mentioned earlier, questionnaires and simple survey forms allow companies to rapidly and cost-effectively train their employees and line managers to recognize the early signs and symptoms of cumulative trauma disorders. The questionnaires isolate the affected body part and rate the magnitude and frequency of any pain or discomfort. Managers are often concerned that the distribution of such questionnaires fosters an increase in the report of injuries or problems from the employees. In my experience they are correct. However, such an increase is short-term. Questionnaires serve the company in the long-run by providing a kind of early warning system to more costly and disabling work related injuries.

Training in workplace assessment techniques. Company training in workplace assessment techniques yields the greatest potential return on investment from productivity enhancements only if sensible recommendations from such assessments are rapidly implemented. Management is strongly advised not to perform workplace assessments until the budget or commitment to implement potential workplace improvements has been approved. Training of safety and engineering staff to perform quantitative, ergonomic workplace assessments that are solution- rather than problem-oriented can, if executed properly, avert costly productivity, injury, and litigation problems. Training in workplace assessment is especially worthwhile if the company has talented engineering and maintenance staff ready and empowered to implement and refine practical workstation modifications. Keep in mind, most workstation modifications consist of the redesign, trial, and refinement of handheld tools. There are numerous corporate and governmental sources for ergonomic training, including nonpunitive OSHA training and inspections. Training in workplace assessment normally takes between one and five days, depending on the skills, education, and previous training of safety and engineering staff. For example, Sikorsky Aircraft implemented an ergonomics training program to outfit their engineering and safety staff with the tools (software and checklists) and practical experience they need to evaluate their workplace jobs and recommend engineering and administrative improvements to reduce injuries. Also Ford, General Motors, U.S. Surgical, AT&T, DuPont, Dow Corning, and many others have done the same.

Posture and exercise training. A third type of training attempts to instruct individuals in correct movement, such as correct lifting, correct assembly, and so on. These training programs are, for the most part, a big waste of time and money. For example, even if the trainer knows there is a correct lifting technique, it is useless to the employee. If they execute the technique perfectly, the forces the body is exposed to may be greater than those their weakest joint or body part can tolerate, either instantaneously or cumulatively. Millions of employees worldwide have undergone training in correct lifting techniques, yet for the past thirty years back injuries have steadily increased.

These types of training programs don't work because correct body movement technique depends on the position and situation the body is in at any given moment. Further, the range of efficacy for injury prevention as a function of correct technique is quite narrow. From a return-on-investment perspective for a company, I would cancel all technique-oriented training programs whose goal is to prevent joint injuries, such as back or wrist injuries. In short, technique training programs geared to prevent cumulative musculoskeletal injuries are basically ineffective. Such money could be used more wisely in aggressively measuring and reducing workplace stressors known to contribute to the development of injury.

However, programs that enhance strength and flexibility, combined with and classified under the rubric of warm-up exercise, are beneficial to the worker. Muscles, tendons, ligaments, and fascia need to stretch gently to increase their dynamic range and reduce the likelihood of stained and stiff muscles. Warm-ups serve the same purpose for any athletic activity. They are a necessary, common-sense preparation needed to limber up muscles and joints to perform activity effectively.

Muscle biofeedback. Muscle biofeedback is actually another form of training. Muscles generate most of the larger forces that our body joints experience throughout the day. The optimization (minimization) of these muscle forces can go a long way to reducing cumulative work exposures. To optimize these muscle forces effectively, it is necessary for the individual to "hear" the muscle working. EMG biofeedback is currently the only technique that allows the user to instantly evaluate the joint stress exposure as a function of muscle contraction and not as a function of pain.

Preplacement Screening

A great deal of attention, concern, and confusion exists around the issue of preplacement screening. Let's focus on the punch line. Does it work? The answer, at best, is sometimes. Several problems with the theory, cost, implementation, and legal requirements of preplacement screening render the technique all but obsolete for noncritical activities.

To properly determine if an applicant is capable of performing a specific job, it is necessary to determine the job requirements, evaluate the applicant, and compare the result. Job requirements can easily be determined. However, measuring the physical ability of the applicant is fraught with difficulty. It is nearly impossible to predict whether or not an applicant will get an injury. Also, the applicant is a dynamic entity, who changes over time, which necessitates re-evaluating the individual at least yearly.

There is a further difficulty when screening and determining an applicant's physical ability. According to the Americans with Disabilities Act (ADA), employers must not discriminate against potential employees with disabilities. Between 43 and 45 million employees in the U.S. are covered by the Americans with Disabilities Act (Scheid 1992) (see Figure 7-17). According to the ADA, a person with a disability is defined as (Section 3(2) Schneid 1992):

Test 1: Has a physical or mental impairment that substantially limits one or more of his or her major life activities.

Test 2: Has a record of such an impairment; or

Test 3: Is regarded as having such an impairment.

According to Schneid:

A physical impairment is defined by the ADA as any physiological disorder or condition, cosmetic disfigurement, or anatomical loss affecting one or more of the following body symptoms: neurological, musculoskeletal, special sense organs, respiratory (including speech organs), cardiovascular, reproductive, digestive, genito-urinary, hemic and lymphatic, skin, and endocrine.

Figure 7-17. Percent of U.S. Population Covered by the Americans with Disabilities Act

If a job requirement exceeds the abilities of the individual, reasonable accommodations must be made to allow the challenged person to perform the task. What is reasonable and who determines it is further complicated by the difficulty of assessing the cost-benefit analysis. What is clear is that a company does not want to run afoul of the ADA when the Justice Department is responsible for upholding the statutes. Consequently, employers cannot discriminate against anyone who has a physical, psychological or cognitive disability. The Americans with Disabilities Act will probably continue to be one of the most enduring programs from the great society legislation of the twentieth century.

In review, preplacement screening based on physical abilities has many shortcomings, such as the:

• Inaccuracy in determining an individual's likelihood of future injury.

• Legally defensible position of reasonable accommodation.

- Ever-changing condition of the individual—and the job for that matter.

- Need for continuous assessments.

In light of this, companies are advised to stay away from this expensive, useless, and potentially litigious endeavor.

Workplace Assessments

Ergonomic workplace assessment is the technique of choice for reducing musculoskeletal injuries and their associated costs. There are numerous approaches for performing these assessments, but the goal is usually the same; *quantify workplace exposures and their associated risks while minimizing expense.* Quality and price tradeoffs occupy a rather narrow range as the discipline has recently emerged. Organizations should use only certified professional ergonomists (CPEs) much as one would use CPAs for conducting significant fiscal audits. It rarely makes economic sense for all but the largest companies to employ full-time ergonomists, as high quality and diverse expertise is usually available from consulting practices and university centers. Most insurance companies offer ergonomic services through their risk management groups. Liberty Mutual is well-known for their forward-thinking ergonomics research center in Hopkington, Massachusetts.

By and large, though, ergonomic assessments are at the stage of blood testing laboratories in the 1930s when most blood was drawn, evaluated, and documented by the physician in charge. The quality was as variable as the skills of the practitioner and the methods and reports were not standardized. A major improvement in the blood testing protocol was developed by Dr. Brown, founder of Metpath, Inc. His vision was to separate data collection from data analysis. This took physicians out of the collection loop and concentrated their expertise where it was needed most—in the laboratory. The result was a dramatic increase in productivity, consistency, quality, and cost reduction. Basically, a blood analysis factory was developed, which was further enhanced by capital investments in equipment to leverage the hematologists knowledge and mechanize the screening process even further. Most scientifically based laboratory assessment programs, for example, air sampling, water testing, and soil testing, have embarked on similar courses of service evolution.

Centralization of the laboratory and the distribution of data collection to less skill intensive practitioners already at the field locations, is a next logical step in the laboratory-based assessment of workplaces. One company, BCAM International, Inc., developed such a program; others undoubtedly will follow. BCAM International used this laboratory-based workplace assessment service to perform hundreds of assessments for major corporations throughout the U.S.

This is the logical direction for optimizing quality and minimizing cost of service. These programs begin with the systematic collection of information concerning workplace exposures. The following flowchart indicates categories of data, analysis, and recommendations that are usually presented (see Figure 7-18).

Workplace and Tool Modifications

The focus of ergonomic workplace assessment is to identify the job or process associated with injuries as well as poor productivity. The next step is to implement a systematic approach for measuring the exposures. The final goal is to develop a plan of action to cost-effectively reduce the unproductive exposures to cumulative musculoskeletal stress. More often than not this means developing an improved product, tool, or process design. Companies with capable engineering staffs may utilize their in-house resources to develop the recommended solutions and

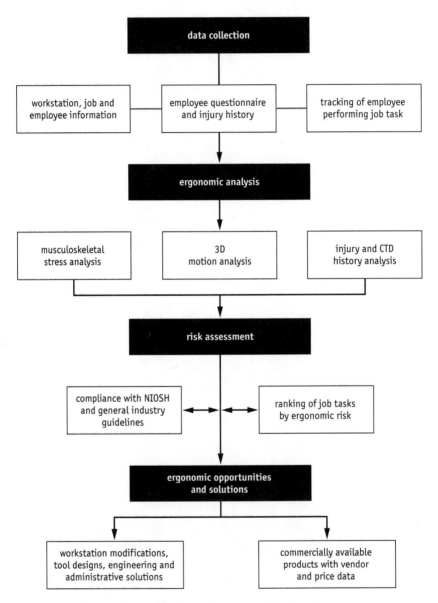

Figure 7.18. Ergonomic Data Acquisition Process

modifications. Few outsiders have the industry-specific expertise to run these tool and process improvement projects. It's best to form an in-house engineering team dedicated to eradicating ergonomic deficiencies in the production environment. In my experience, the cost of performing the surveys and assessments is usually less than 5 percent of the cost of developing the solutions. Successful, accurate, and rapid development of solutions is the determinate factor in effectively dealing with injuries and poor productivity. These solutions often require significant capital investments that necessitate careful return on investment evaluations before implementing the program. For example, a major pharmaceutical manufacturer's production line cost $25,000 to evaluate, but it cost $470,000 to implement the modifications to improve productivity and reduce worker discomfort and injury potential. The potential savings from such an investment are 30 to 60 percent reduction in injury costs per annum following implementation.

THE COST OF INACTION

Humanitarian reasons aside, workplace ergonomics is all about reducing costs. A simplified history of the concerns of plant managers during the past thirty years can be written as follows:

- Produce as much as you can, as quickly as possible, at the lowest cost.

- Produce as much as you need of world class quality products at the lowest cost.

- Produce as much as you need of world class quality products at the lowest cost, and *safely*.

The added concern of safely producing products creates a paradox for the manager. How do you maximize productivity safely? Add safety into the equation of productivity, and confusion immediately results, raising some very tough, seemingly unanswerable questions. What is safe? How do I measure it? What is the cost of safety? What are acceptable risks? What is required by law, sensibility, conscience, or our shareholders?

Besides the safety issues, companies are still confronted with this undeniable fact: *The most expensive, unmanaged manufacturing cost in the world results from cumulative, musculoskeletal injuries.* In the U.S. in 1994, the cost of back injury was estimated at 30 billion dollars. That is $300 for each working person in the U.S. each year. Now add wrist injuries, elbow injuries, and knee injuries, and a picture of tremendous waste emerges. This kind of waste reduces the competitive advantage of a company as well as a nation. It also produces a great deal of needless pain and suffering for the worker.

Action and inaction may be viewed on the same scale that defines the human motivation of obtaining rewards or avoiding punishments. Companies that fail to act on cumulative musculoskeletal injuries are not avoiding punishment. The brutal fact is that these kinds of injuries are taking away from the value of your product and the long-term value of your organization. Dr. Taguchi provides an imaginative analogy when he defines the quality of a manufactured product as the loss to society that the product creates. His focus on the negative aspects of a product underscores the need for a balanced view of production and safety. A vehicle assembly plant cannot produce vehicles successfully if the process induces significant workplace injuries and disabilities. Even from a purely economical point of view, the above statement would be true.

Often companies don't account for injuries in the cost of goods. This is a big mistake. A typical back injury may cost $10,000 in lost time and medical treatment. When the indirect costs are factored in, such as retraining, claims management, reduced productivity, and legal costs, the $10,000 can easily double. When you consider the 70 percent recurrence rates associated with back injuries and combine this with a twenty-five year employment history, it is easy to see how this episodic back injury could cost the organization $400,000. Now view the added value of the product in this cost context. What impact does this have on the organization's success now? By designing a workstation that fits employees, an organization can save on medical cost, as well as turn the wasted, harmful motions of their workers into actual productive work.

Ergonomics As Your Safety Program

To be thus nothing; but to be safely thus.
—William Shakespeare, *Macbeth* (1606)

To prevent cumulative musculoskeletal injuries, ergonomics makes good business sense, both financially and in terms of contributing to a healthier, happier workforce. The first step in developing an ergonomics program is to develop a written plan. It should outline the program goals, management, methods and evaluation criteria. A typical manufacturing ergonomics plan consists of the following elements.

A. Program Goals
1. Develop ergonomics leadership in your industry.
2. Foster ergonomics sensibility and awareness at all company levels.
3. Establish a corporate ergonomics resource to develop solutions and monitor the program.
4. Establish, train, equip, and motivate the ergonomics task force.
5. Develop in-house ergonomics engineering and design capabilities.

B. Management Commitment and Employee Involvement

1. Develop a written ergonomics program (business plan).

2. Top management must demonstrate enthusiasm and commitment.

3. Delegate authority and responsibility to frontline employees.

4. Conduct regular and quantitative program reviews.

C. Major Program Elements

1. Work-site analysis

   a. Identify ergonomic hazards (surveys).

   b. Perform quantitative work-site assessments.

   c. Produce and distribute ergonomic reports to all task force members.

2. Comfort enhancement, hazard prevention, and control

   a. Engineering controls

      1. Workstation design

      2. Design of work methods

      3. Tool design

   b. Work practice controls

      1. Proper work techniques

      2. Monitoring and feedback

      3. Work rotation

   c. Evaluate and use personal protective equipment

   d. Administrative controls

3. Medical Management

   a. Properly train accessible health care providers.

   b. Administer symptom surveys (musculoskeletal questionnaires).

   c. Compile standard job descriptions.

   d. Develop diagnostic protocols for health care providers.

   e. Develop procedures for systematic injury evaluation,
      treatment, follow-up, and early return to work.

   f. Maintain a database of injury and illness records and
      provide data regularly to task force members and senior
      management.

4. Training and Education

   a. Training employees at risk (following statistical
      evaluation of injury surveillance data).

   b. Train managers, supervisors, and engineering and
      medical personnel.

   c. Have supervisors training for line employees.

Another added advantage of an ergonomics manufacturing safety
program is that a company can usually incorporate it into their existing
TQM program, using many of the same staff.

WHAT YOU SHOULD KNOW

1. Workplace ergonomics is the science that seeks to design workplace tasks, conditions, and tools to fit the worker. The basic concept is that reducing both physical and psychological stress on the body (through improved employee comfort) will likely reduce workplace injuries.

2. Musculoskeletal workplace illnesses now comprise 62 percent of all occupational illnesses in the U.S. The cost of back injury in U.S. businesses is about 30 billion dollars per year.

4. In cumulative trauma disorders the muscles are often the culprit in the development of injuries.

5. Ergonomics deals directly with the four elements of cumulative musculoskeletal injuries: force, frequency, posture, and vibration exposure.

6. Most workplace injuries can be prevented, which saves on costs and significantly enhances your pre-tax margins and market capitalization.

WHAT YOU SHOULD DO

1. Conduct a needs assessment to determine the current cost of musculoskeletal illnesses to your organization. As part of this needs analysis, administer the musculoskeletal questionnaire on pages 138 to 140 to a sample of associates across locations. Compare this data with lost time, medical costs, insurance premiums, worker compensation, litigation costs, and claims management costs associated with these illnesses.

2. Based on the current estimated costs of musculoskeletal injuries using present value, return on equity, or effect on market capitalization (or all three), allocate a budget to implement a comprehensive workplace ergonomics program geared to improve productivity and reduce the costs of injuries.

3. Carefully track the program progress and calculate the total benefit to the organization.

8

EQ, TQM, and leadership

To reform means
to shatter one form to create another;
but the two sides of this act
are not always equally intended
nor equally successful.
—G. SANTAYANA

Many companies that have implemented TQM have benefited by eliminating product defects, enhancing product design, speeding delivery of the product, and reducing cost (Shiba, Graham, and Walden, 1993).

There are four basic concepts common to a company's successful implementation of TQM:

1. Focus on the customers and on developing products to satisfy their needs.

2. Seek continuous improvement of the processes that lead to higher quality products and services.

3. Seek total participation of the staff in order to accomplish the first two items.

4. Participate in societal learning to implement quality
   practices more quickly, and to create a quality culture in
   which to do business.

By focusing on the customer to develop products, making products that improve processes, ensuring that quality is built into the product, EQ has similar goals to TQM. It is also building a similar track record of success.

EQ: THE NEXT STEP IN TQM

EQ, like TQM, understands that fulfilling the expectations of customers is the best and only lasting means to business success. This means building the customer as well as quality into the product during the development cycle. Though quality is relative and, therefore, always subject to perspective and experience, EQ extends the TQM model by attacking the issue of "what quality is" because its focus is to produce products that perform comfortably and safely to the dimensions of the customer. While TQM seeks to create a transparent interface between heretofore separate corporate departments, EQ extends this direct connection to the product-customer relationship, making EQ the logical next step in TQM. EQ can also be seen as the next step in TQM's evolution because it deals directly with customer comfort and safety—making products that fit—ensuring quality, customer satisfaction, and innovation. Yet EQ remains a vast, nearly untouched playing field when it comes to companies building a competitive advantage.

LEADERSHIP AND ITS ROLE IN TQM AND EQ

Quality is like beauty. All would readily agree to its value, yet most would argue its worth. Yet the need for quality is continuously growing. As consumers become more experienced their need and appetite for quality grows. Wall et al., (1992) reported that in a 1978 consumer poll, 30 percent rated quality as more important than price. By 1990, the response to the same poll in the United States was 70 percent. With the loss of market share in the 1980s, senior management quickly learned about the cost of poor quality. They also learned that to survive in the international marketplace they could not continue to focus on results or just manage workers. Instead, they had to develop new leadership tactics. One such tactic was to emulate the Japanese model of success, focusing on methods of continuous improvement and customer-oriented TQM. TQM is all about the leadership role of top management in the quality control movement.

In their excellent book on TQM, Besterfield et. al., (1995) define six points for effective leadership:

1. People need security and independence.

2. People are self-motivated, as well as sensitive to external rewards.

3. People like to hear a kind word or phrase.

4. People can process only a few facts at a time—keep it simple.

5. People trust their gut reaction more than statistical data.

6. People distrust a leader whose words are inconsistent with his or her actions.

Decision Making by Concensus

Leadership is all about empowerment with a purpose. Leadership styles are culturally varied. The most successful leader formulates a leadership strategy that fits the sensibilities of the team. In the United States, that sensibility can best be stated as "create and encourage." This kind of team approach is consensus after the fact, which differs from the coalition approach to global decision making. Here the group must find the path to organizational success while the strategic map is developed by the leader. The strategy is a perspective, after all, and no committee can expect to compete and win against a razor-sharp, imaginative leadership perspective. The consensus enters later and works best in the execution, where individual strengths can be leveraged and weaknesses made irrelevant. By maintaining a balance or harmony among perspectives, the consensus approach answers certain questions more completely than could individual inspiration. What is the best way to do this? How can we improve this design?

Strategy Through Inspired Leadership

The purpose of inspired leadership, however, is not to focus on creating harmony, but rather to stake a claim on a specific vision. Harmony comes later, after the merit and power of the new direction are digested and inculcated into the organization's present way of thinking. Inspired, personalized leadership may be a primitive approach to designing strategy, but it is necessary if organizations are to make sense of and find purpose in the infinite paths there are to choose from.

Max DuPree, the former CEO of Herman Miller, offers a definition of inspired leadership:

> The first responsibility of a leader is to define reality. The last is to say thank you. In between the two, the leader must become a servant and a debtor.

Mr. DuPree, in his book, *Leadership is an Art,* identifies the following traits in leaders:

- Has consistent and dependable integrity

- Cherishes heterogeneity and diversity

- Searches out competence

- Is open to contrary opinion

- Communicates easily at all levels

- Understands the concept of equity and consistently advocates it

- Leads through serving

- Is vulnerable to the skills and talents of others

- Is intimate with the organization and its work

- Is able to see the broad picture

- Is a spokesperson and diplomat

Leadership is also the courage to take a position, formulate a vision, and execute it. Leadership is a test of the quality of your vision and your strength of character. Leadership is required to manage change. In *The Visionary Leader,* Wall et al. define three stages of vision-induced personal change (see Figure 8-1):

The *Ending* is defined as the initial catharsis whose starting point allows us to make the departure into a new vision. It seems appropriate

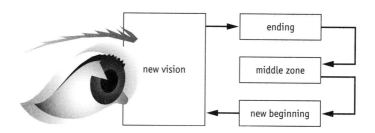

Figure 8-1. Three Stages of Vision-Induced Personal Change

that a new vision would begin with a clarification of the ending. For example, Leonardo DaVinci's *The Virgin on the Rocks* (c 1507), which clarified the classical world so well and empowered others like Henri Matisse to move beyond classical painting with "Le Luxe II" (c 1907). Most classical and romantic symphonies use a recapitulation to help clear the way for the next movement. The effect often evokes a feeling of loss. At the very least, it means taking away what is familiar and forcing you to deal with another movement with its new approach, method, or view.

The *Middle Zone* marks the beginning success of the voyage, including the frustration of having to try and discard many new ideas until a good fit can be found.

The *New Beginning* is the successful navigation of change, the launching point to move you into a new challenge.

Of course, the three stages of vision-induced, personal change are a continuous cycle and it is the successful, inspiring leader who can empower others to make this trip often. A good leader must be able to attract, absorb, reconstitute, and rechannel psychic energy to inspire others to manifest their complete capabilities in the context of the organization's mission.

ERGONOMICS AND LEADERSHIP

> If poetry comes not as naturally
> as the leaves to a tree
> it had better not come at all.
> —JOHN KEATS, 1818

To be successful, top management must concentrate on the strengths of individuals, as well as the strengths of their countries. The main point, according to a recent book by Clifton and Nelson (1992), is to focus on your own strengths. The authors' strategy is two-fold:

- Find out what you do well and do more of it.

- Find out what you don't do well and stop doing it.

In a sense, this is exactly what has been happening in the United States in the past three decades. Currently, industrial manufacturing accounts for 17.6 percent of GDP (Gross Domestic Product) in the United States. In 1983 the amount was 20.36 percent and in 1973, it was 24.27 percent. Figure 8-2 shows the international percent of GNP derived from manufacturing.

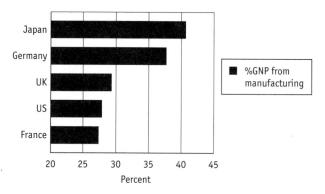

Figure 8-2. Percent GNP Derived from Manufacturing

It is clear that manufacturing is going the way of farming, which last century was the largest U.S. employer (53 percent of the population in 1870) but now occupies less than 5 percent of the population. It is the service sector that is now booming. The United States, using its strength as an innovator, is finding new ways to enter this market as the manufacturing base shrinks. This cultural innovative strength should be kept in mind as you develop your mission statements.

According to Wall et al (1992), the traditional mission statement attempts to answer the questions:

- Who are we?

- What do we do?

- For whom do we do it?

- Why do we do it?

We must, however add one more to the list:

- How do we do it?

An inspired leader develops an insightful mission statement that aims high for excellence, quality, and market dominance, but the statement should also address the how—the process that will get you there. Ergonomic quality is all about the "how." Because EQ is customer-oriented (service), not product-oriented (manufacturing), it naturally extends itself into a function of leadership. A company requires innovative and inspired leadership to shift from a product-oriented process to a customer-oriented process. Try inserting the word ergonomics in your mission statement, it will say a lot about how to achieve excellence, quality, and market dominance.

EQ exemplifies the evolution away from manufacturing in a vacuum to manufacturing in the growing service context. A good example of this is the shift from a hardware focus to a software focus in the computer industry. The software touches the customer. The same has occurred in the watch industry. When the mechanism was the focus, the Swiss dominated the world market for watches. With programmed microprocessors, the Japanese dominate the world market for watches. They produce watches that are, in some cases, several orders of magnitude less expensive, yet have greater accuracy and require less service than their mechanical counterparts. EQ defines the product interface—the part of the product that touches the customer. In the greater scheme of things, EQ is the new process tool for directly delivering customer satisfaction as well as a practical strategy for top management to keep their customers and products moving in harmony for optimal profits.

ENCOURAGING TOTAL EMPLOYEE INVOLVEMENT

Charming spot. Inspiring projects. Let's go.
—SAMUEL BECKETT (1955)

Most enlightened employees are volunteers. The way the knowledge-based society is now structured, the power to act and the information needed to act have become temporarily separate—they will coalesce in time. Meanwhile, when companies are making information-intensive decisions they need to consult information-intensive individuals, or employees. Not consulting with or including these employees in the decision loop in some form of participatory management is like your brain not consulting your feet while you're running.

With enlightened, volunteer employees you also have mobile employees. One way to keep these employees and regain some of the sense of loyalty that has been lost during the downsizing of corporations is to provide them with a working atmosphere that is conducive to being productive and happy. As discussed earlier, workplace ergonomics helps an employee become both safer and more productive. But a worker needs to be satisfied also. Without satisfied employees, it is impossible to have satisfied customers. The underbelly of customer delight is employee delight.

Empowering the Employee for Maximum Achievement

In *The Wow Factory,* Paul Levesque (1995) presents a brilliant, yet simple solution to the old saw, "That sounds good but how do we achieve it?" The answer is, make work fun. What is fun? Webster defines it as enjoyment, pleasure, or that which provides mirth or amusement. Yet, with the exception of Intel, few of the corporate mission statements from major companies include the words enjoyment or fun in the context of either their employees' attitude towards work or their customers' attitude towards their products or services. Winning businesses can be very enjoyable. Outmaneuvering a competitor and outperforming a market leader are analogous to the thrill of the hunt and ought to be enjoyed as much as watching the Yankees recapture the World Series.

However, the major reason organizations should engage in participatory management is the mutual self-actualization that it encourages. Beyond Maslow's traditional hierarchy, the new goal is empowerment for maximum achievement. This new order needs to be the underlying basis for corporate and individual growth, a growth that is a waltz of capabilities and opportunities. Empowerment for maximum achievement is all about having the opportunity to find and surpass your limits. At its best, a corporation rapidly expands if it is able to resonate the capabilities of its employees, in harmony with the needs of its customers. The degree of somatic resonance in a company is often measured by sales per employee. Another valuable measure for innovative companies is sales per employee by patent, especially for those companies that have brutal, technology-driven competition. Of the top patent-producing companies in the U.S. 1994, Ford Motor Company led the nation in sales per employee by patent (see Figure 8-3).

All of the companies listed in Figure 8-3 are strong in the classic sense; however, Ford is particularly gifted at transforming patented developments into sales per employee. Two by-products of this ability

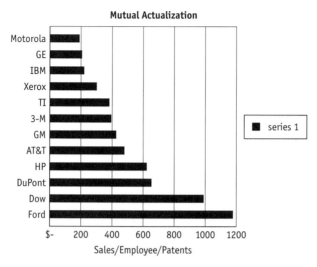

Figure 8-3. Sales Per Employee by Patent

have been a significant increase in market share and an improvement in product quality. Other measures, such as percent of total revenue from new products and services, are also valuable indicators of ongoing employee-company synergy. All of these valuable measures can immediately tell you how well your company is encouraging, harnessing, and benefiting from human power, a human power that comes from *mutual actualization.*

One way for organizations to achieve this and have a heads-on in addition to hands-on experience is to reverse the traditional corporate structure. There is little time or room left for traditional staff-line structures. As Mears recommends (1995), *flip the organization,* however difficult this may seem at first (see Figure 8-4).

Specifically, executives need to:

• Provide information to frontline employees.

• Create a customer orientation for all employees. Martin

Traditional Corporate Structure

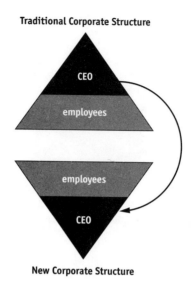

New Corporate Structure

Figure 8-4. Flipping the Traditional Corporate Structure

Buber would refer to this as I and Thou. All company members are "I's" and all customer's are "Thou's."

• Push down and delegate authority to the front line employees until it hurts.

• Trust your team, they are all you've got.

With TQM, customer focus permeates throughout the company, making all employees at all levels potential customers. In this way, everyone in the company is encouraged to perform their skills adeptly, while focusing on satisfying changing customer needs. This total employee involvement process elevates everyone into a participant and helps to make the company successful. In this regard, it's the executive's job to remind employees continuously that customer satisfaction is the purpose of their work.

With its innovative emphases, ergonomic quality thrives in, if not creates, an atmosphere of mutual actualization. Innovation harnesses the capabilities of the employees and seizes the opportunities born from them. By also using customer-centered product development, ergonomic quality seeks out and captures the optimism that comes from including the customer and the employee in the process of product design. This mutual exchange between employee and customer should add an element of fun and adventure for the whole company.

BUILDING STRATEGIC ALLIANCES WITH SUPPLIERS, DISTRIBUTORS, AND PARTNERSHIPS

In 1982, I gave a paper at the Photo-Optical Engineering Society. The guest speaker during the society dinner was Colonel Mattingly, a Space Shuttle astronaut. During an informal question and answer period, I asked him what it felt like when he first stepped into the shuttle. He said, "It was an awesome feeling to know that these hundreds of thousands of sophisticated components were all built by the lowest bidder."

As Dr. Deming and others have said, it is important not to select suppliers based solely upon price, because price has no meaning without quality. But, current partnerships with suppliers should go way beyond the price issue. A company should select a partner because they are best able to provide a product or service that your company needs. They not only should do it better than you can do it, but they should do it the best in their industry. A company should select them because they have the knowledge and experience. This is what translates into the long-term product and cost advantage—your suppliers are your partners. Though a company should have as few as is necessary, suppliers should be viewed as strategic alliances, not commodity houses. *The goal of a successful strategic alliance is to make each others' weaknesses irrelevant.*

Companies that use ergonomic quality standards should require their suppliers to do likewise. Specifically, all products and services provided should:

- Incorporate optimized human interfaces (feel great).

- Include objective assessments of customer use compared with similar products from other marketplace leaders.

- Measure and document ease of product/service use and user comfort for major customer groups.

- Be safe to use (not contribute to musculoskeletal stress or injury).

The assumption of mutual responsibility for ergonomic quality is a basic element to help ensure success between suppliers. Companies would benefit from certifying and rating suppliers according to their ergonomic capabilities.

MEASURING PERFORMANCE

Measurement is vital to all activities, yet it is often overvalued or extrapolated beyond the appropriate limits of what is being measured. As Werner Heisenberg observed in the Uncertainty Principle, the act of observation affects what one is attempting to measure. Specifically, the more accurate you are in determining the position of a particle, the less accurate you become in measuring and determining the momentum, and vice-versa. In fact, the uncertainty between position and momentum is linked by Planck's Constant. There are inherent limitations to physical knowledge; this is a fact well demonstrated by twentieth century physics. This limitation on measurement can be applied to the operations of a workplace. Before measuring a company's management or employee performance, we must ask ourselves some tough questions. One in particular is, how do you measure performance?

What Determines Great Performance?

Is great performance selling 10 million dollars worth of postage machines, or selling the first fax machine at great pain, expense, and effort? In determining great performance, companies need to do more than use measurement to count the results. Measurement is as far beyond counting as wisdom is beyond information. Measurement needs to be applied appropriately and wisely in relation to the circumstances being measured. For instance, when measuring the cost/benefits of innovation you cannot view the results in the same way you would from a continuous improvement or TQM perspective. Innovation, relies on discontinuous as opposed to continuous improvement. It is an interruption of the normal business cycle or status quo. Innovation and the means of attaining it through ergonomic quality go beyond the main focus of continuous improvement and TQM, though the maintenance of innovation requires continuous improvement. So how do you measure the great performance of innovation—of the fax machine as opposed to the postage machine, of the what is possible to the what already is? An inspired leader understands these differences, recalibrates the measuring yardstick and judges the performance of each aspect of the company accordingly. In this sense, great performance is relative to what you are measuring.

Problem Solving: Flying Fish Approach

Great performance demands great action as well as great results. Problem solving, or as my uncle would say, turning a sack of lemons into lemonade, is one type of great action. I call this great action process the flying fish paradigm (see Figure 8-5). Traditional cause and effect diagrams illustrate the principle of tracking down root causes. The old saw of "necessity being the mother of invention" holds true in these diagrams. But with the flying fish technique, the problem of identifying

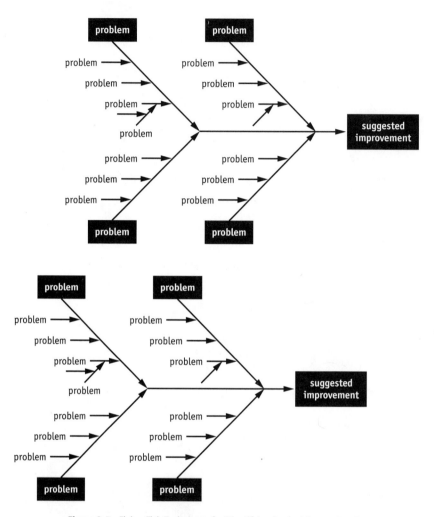

Figure 8-5. Flying Fish Techniques for Identifying Product Improvements

root causes turns instead into a very useful tool for the identification of improvements. This process can quickly escalate into bouts of innovation as team synergy turns problem after problem into potential improvements.

A brutally objective assessment of customers' ergonomic needs and problems with a company's products, coupled with implementation of the flying fish technique for identifying product improvements, greatly speeds up the product development process.

Problem Solving: Generating Options

In his excellent short book on problem solving, Dr. Noone (1993) stresses the need for ideas and lots of them to solve problems. The reason is that the generation of ideas poses questions and these questions in turn generate options, or at the very least, a better understanding of what is not known. To help facilitate these ideas Dr. Noone recommends asking a continuous series of questions geared to generate and make apparent many of your options. Fittingly, Dr. Noone's checklist is called the *Option Generator*. The questions/options are as follows:

Adapt

How can we use something that works elsewhere?

What can we copy? Or imitate?

What might be suitable if modified?

How have others solved this or similar problems? Our vendors? Our customers? Our competitors?

How would people in other disciplines solve it? Cultures?

How can we turn our problem into an opportunity?

What two or more things, if joined, would make something new? People? Products? Technologies? Services? Materials? Functions? Organizations? Inventions?

Streamline

In what way can we make the process leaner? Smoother?

How can we make it more responsive? More direct?

What are the precious things that have outlived their
usefulness?

What can be eliminated?

What can be compressed? Or bypassed?

What can be ignored?

What one format can be used with many variations?

How can we make our service/product more appealing?

How can we achieve and keep high levels of customer
satisfaction?

How can the frequency of customized or special products
be reduced? Or increased?

How can we use an express line? Do more with less?

Reorganize

In what ways can the elements be set up differently?

How can they be rearranged? Rescheduled?

How can we alter established priorities?

Can we start at the end?

Can we do just the opposite?

Can the way to solve this problem begin from the inside out?

How can we rotate the elements?

What could be a surprise or unexpected result?

What other materials can be used? Procedures? Processes?
Markets? Technologies? Suppliers? Locations? Persons?

What new targets can we establish?

Change

In what ways can we speed up?

How can we magnify our impact?

In what ways can we add value to other functions?

How can we multiply the number of positive ripples we
    send out?

How can we put more sizzle into what we're selling?

How can we get more visibility?

In what ways can we raise quality?

How can we achieve zero defects?

How can we give customers more than they expect?

Are there obstacles we can remove? Minimize?

Are there things that can be reduced? Made smaller?
    Condensed?

Would it make any sense to slow down?

Are there things we can subtract? Divide? Break up?

How can we lower the cost?

How can we decrease response time? Shorten intervals?

How can we lessen customer complaints?

How can we help those we serve become more successful?

What else?

What else could it be used for?

Are there new markets for out services? Products?

Suppose our capability was portable? Mobile?

Does our expertise suggest any spin-offs? In other fields?

What needs exist in the marketplace that our skill could
    address? For individuals? Families? Organizations? Others?

How can we enrich the lives of our associates with our
    capability?

How can we change the meaning of what we do? The setting?

The attitudes and habits of those on board?

How can we alter the reward system? Change policy?

How can we use time more effectively?

How can we differentiate our function? Distinguish it?

How can we alter perceptions of others and persuade them great things are happening?

How can we improve what we do?

How can we get colleagues to feel they are a part of the team?

Paradoxical Thinking

How can we worsen an already difficult situation?

How can we snatch defeat from the jaws of victory?

How can we close the window of opportunity?

How can we let things slip through the cracks?

How can we really get cemented into our present position?

What can we do to make the losses greater?

What if . . . Scenarios

What if we discover a new way?

What if we blithely ignore the problem?

What if we accept the first solution that pops into mind?

What if we take a very conservative posture?

What if we try . . . ?

The above questions ought to be asked to force the issue and stimulate an idea or direction to solve the problem at hand. Questions are the embryos of solutions. The disciplined, openminded person questions everything before staking out a vantage point. By being brutally objective, you can lessen the baggage of incomplete or emotion-laden ideas.

PROCESS SKILLS

Skepticism is the chastity of the intellect.

—G. SANTAYANA

As we continue to become a knowledge-based society, process skills will become increasingly more important for determining individual and corporate success. In David Stamp's recent work entitled *The Invisible Assembly Line,* he defines eight main categories of process-related skills:

1. Vision/value

2. Thinking strategically

3. Focusing resources

4. Managing priorities

5. Meeting performance expectations

6. Taking ownership

7. Influencing others

8. Striving for continuous improvement

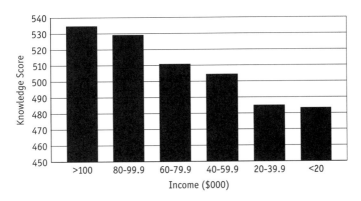

Figure 8-6. Relationship Between Income and Knowledge

Stamps' book describes a study of more than 8,000 individuals that found a significant correlation between process knowledge and income (see Figure 8-6). Clearly, to earn well it is necessary to learn well.

Elements of Personal Success

In a 1993 study by the Families and Work Institute, individuals were asked to respond to more than one factor that constituted success at work (see Figure 8-7). What was the result? Eighty-two percent of the responses defined success at work as entailing *personal satisfaction* and *earning respect*. Job advancement opportunities and making a good income constituted 43 percent of the responses. This brings us back around to the employee's need for self-actualization.

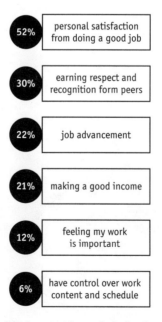

Figure 8-7. Important Factors in Feeling Successful

Successful companies moving into the next century will employ individuals for their specific expertise, who are both process-sensitive and knowledgeable about the company's customers and products.

WHAT YOU SHOULD KNOW

1. EQ is the next logical step in TQM because it deals directly with customers' comfort and safety—making products that fit—ensuring quality, customer satisfaction, and innovation.

2. Great leadership is required to shift an organization from a product focus to a customer-oriented, process focus. Ergonomic Quality (EQ) naturally extends itself into a function of leadership because it is customer-centered— building the customer as well as quality into the product during the development cycle.

3. A good leader must be able to inspire others to manifest their complete capabilities in the context of the organization's mission.

4. When companies are making information-intensive decisions they need to consult knowledgeable information-intensive employees.

5. Mutual actualization results in delivering innovation to customers. With its innovative emphases, EQ thrives in, if not creates, an atmosphere of mutual actualization.

6. Suppliers should be viewed as strategic alliances, not commodity houses.

WHAT YOU SHOULD DO

1. Flip the organizational chart. Associates that deal with customers must have the authority to satisfy those customers.

2. Figure out your core competencies, focus on them, and make sure the manifestations of your strengths, be they services or products, are ergonomically correct. Shed the nonessential and buy or partner all supporting services.

3. Measure how well your company is encouraging, harnessing, and benefiting from human (employee) power.

9

EQ: a global strategy for marketplace leadership

Freedom is always and exclusively freedom
for the one who thinks differently.
—ROSA LUXEMBURG, *DIE RUSSISCHE REVOLUTION* (1918)

To differentiate your company in the marketplace with a strategic
management policy, base your strategy for success on leveraging
your strengths and making your weaknesses irrelevant. The global
competition for mainstream products and services will be unimaginably
more difficult in the next ten years. For products and services to continuously improve, yet remain cost effective, it will be necessary for
them to be knowledge based. As knowledge is the new capital, the new
means of production, companies that can add value to information
through structure or material will have the opportunity to dominate
entire market segments.

WORLD CLASS PRODUCTS

Ergonomics is a key strategy that will enable companies to channel their
development efforts to maximize productivity and profit margins. World
class products in the twenty-first century will have to be built with levels of integration, ease of use and efficiency that is not easily imagined
today. Similarly, the information and knowledge content of these

products is expanding far faster than many organizations can hope to assimilate. It will be no more possible to own the knowledge source for your enterprise than it is to own a significant portion of a commodity such as gold. The best to hope for is the use of other people's knowledge through strategic alliances and loose, information-need relationships. In this context, ergonomics will play an increasing role in the determination of product and services interfaces, and in defining the relationships between people and the tools they use. Ergonomics is knowledge-intensive, not cost-intensive. Corporate expertise in ergonomics is ideally suited for a product and service differentiation strategy.

Academia as a Strategic Alliance

One largely untapped avenue for strategic alliances resides with universities. There is a unique opportunity for companies to engage with these would-be development teams for knowledge and inspiration concerning all phases of product/service development and manufacture. To mutually survive, universities will become more like knowledge centers (some say they already are) and companies will become exclusive merchandisers of particular subdisciplines of these knowledge centers. The result will be a new marriage of necessity between academia and industry, whereby they might make each other's weaknesses irrelevant and the duplication of expensive capital, infrastructure, and manpower investments will become unnecessary. It would be highly cost-effective for organizations to contact their local university and speak to an expert in their area of need. More than ever, the different university departments are willing and available to help you.

Retraining employees is another way companies can use universities. In the next twenty years, as process improvements continue to connect the customer directly to the organization, even more middle management positions will be eliminated. An imaginative barter strategy incorporating tuition remission as a perk for contract research could dramatically reduce product/service development costs, and increase the head-count flexibility of your organization while paring severance costs. It would also retrain these individuals so they can be gainfully employed and continue to contribute to society.

Design for Excellence

The considerations for developing a world class product span all traditional engineering and customer concerns (see Figure 9-1).

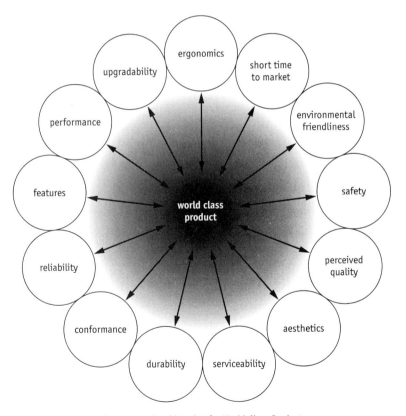

Figure 9-1. Consideration for World-Class Products

Each of these aspects must be evaluated, measured, compared, and balanced to achieve product greatness. All must be assessed rapidly as well, to help ensure maximal market share penetration gains. Bralla (1996) refers to this as DFX or "Design for Excellence."

Traditionally we measure the research and development focus by the percent of sales a company spends on R&D. Table 9-1 shows a sample of some industry-specific expenditures that reveal what is by now an obvious fact—those industries with larger percentages are growing more rapidly. These are the sector innovators.

Table 9-1. R&D as a Percent of Sales

Industry	R&D as % of Sales
Software & Services	13.2
Health care (drugs and research)	11.5
Computer Communications	11.5
Semiconductors	9.4
Computers	8.8
Medical Products	6.7
Electronics	5.8
Instruments	5.4
Aerospace	4.4
Chemicals	4.3
Cars and Trucks	4.2
Automotive Tire and Rubber	2.6
Business Machines	2.6
Personal Care Products	2.5
Automotive Parts and Equipment	2.4
Machine and hand tools	2.0
Appliances/Home Furnishings	1.9
Housing	1.8
Paper and Forest Products	1.1
Textile Manufacturing	1.0
Containers and Packaging	0.9
Food	0.7
Oil, Gas, and Coal	0.6

As the success of the software, pharmaceutical, and communications industries indicates, greater percentages of gross sales in the future will likely have to be spent on R&D for any industry to achieve a strategic advantage. The cost implications are massive. The equivalent of TQM in product development will have to take place to prevent short-term erosion of low-tech company market capitalization. Ergonomics is just this type of strategy—low cost innovation for companies that provide products and services that come in contact (physical or otherwise) with people.

Beyond continuous improvement lies continuous innovation. This requires the continuous acquisition of knowledge, and lots of it. World class products need to fit the individual, be easy to use, extend the capabilities of the individual, and they must be safe.

Frequent Team Communication

Enhanced communication among development team members is key for compressing development time and stimulating ideas. Not too long ago, distance was a great barrier in team communication. In an interesting study, Dr. Allen, at MIT (1977), found that the distance between team members has a dramatic inverse relationship with the frequency of communication (see Figure 9-2).

It is easy to see the profound implications for workplace improvement that result from using video/audio communications on the Internet to hook up all development team members, world wide, continuously. Smith and Reinertsen (1991) point out that perhaps subconsciously listening to what's being said around you keeps you in a global context with other development team members. Regardless of communication being best between individuals who are less than 30 feet (10 meters), the data speaks strongly to the living, on line video-phone connection. It is important that you keep your development team in touch with each

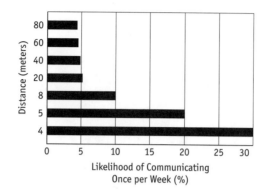

Figure 9-2. Relationship Between Separation Distance and Communication

other continuously, even if they are in the same building on different floors.

WORLD CLASS FACTORIES

There is a true story that Peter Medawar, the British Zoologist, conveyed concerning the Spanish Royal Family. In the 1400s Spain could well have been considered the center of the modern world. She had the dominant naval power, was a center for trade, and in the process, had amassed great wealth. Fittingly, the coat of arms of the Royal Family was a ship sailing between the Pillars of Hercules with the Latin motto inscribed beneath the pillars, *Ne Plus Ultra* (No More Beyond). After Columbus rediscovered America, efficient court advisors rapidly changed the motto to *Plus Ultra*. There is always "more beyond." This is why our plans and endeavors should always be flexible—we never know what new discovery will emerge on the horizon, or what kinds of unintended consequences or implications it may have on the way we go about our daily business. The deeper lesson here is that there is no limit to our explorations and our ability to generate information and synthesize or extract knowledge from it. Our only limitation lies in the application of sensibility, which may be interpreted as a combination of the ability to predict the future and the strength of one's faith and value in the use of those predictions.

Before you can build great products or services you must empower your people with greatness. One way to do this is to inspire them to continuously innovate or redraw the boundaries–to be visionary as well as practical. As technology strengthens and evolves into a knowledge-based capital, manufacturing will become more an act of will, of drawing upon mental resources, rather than an act of physical exertion. Mission plus will and technology will create the new products of the next century. The companies that will succeed are those that will continuously accommodate their customers with the best-designed products, at the lowest cost. This means companies will need to invest in world class factories. These factories with their ergonomic manufacturing workplaces, will design ergonomic products and tools that will, in turn, fabricate other products or provide services that will play an essential role in this development. In more than 100 of the Fortune 500 workplaces I have visited, I have yet to see a factory like this.

DEVELOPING AN ERGONOMIC COMPETITIVE STRATEGY

The new leaders understand one crucial fact: that personal fulfillment and business success cannot be separated.
—BOB WALL, ROBERT SOLUM, AND MARK SOBOL, *THE VISIONARY LEADER*, 1992

The *first step* in developing an ergonomic competitive strategy is for top management to formulate a strategic model or world view. This will allow you and your management team to rapidly see what is available internally and what is missing in your strategic planning tool box (see Figure 9-3). Great product development strengths are often wasted

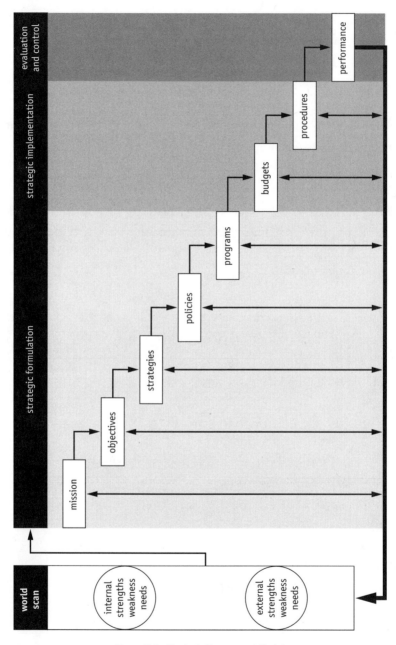

Figure 9-3. Strategic Management Model

because their proponents are forced to compensate for weaknesses in strategic planning.

The *second step* in developing an ergonomic competitive strategy is to create an ergonomics mission statement for your products or services. The focus of the statement should be to accommodate the customer for optimal comfort, ease of use, and safety. An effective ergonomics strategy must be well thought out to provide your product lines with a distinct competitive advantage. *Product differentiation is at the heart of a successful ergonomics strategy.* Pursuing a competitive advantage by keeping the cost of your product low, at best will garner small gains in market share. This kind of cost-only strategy should be reserved for products that are no longer featured, or top of the line. An important part of strategic planning with regard to ergonomic product development is to create the right fit between the product(s) and customer, as well as meet and exceed the ever changing needs and demands of the marketplace. By far, strategic planning is the most important aspect in guaranteeing success in ergonomic product research and development. In *The Art of War,* Sun-tzu says, "The highest realization of warfare is to attack the enemies plans. He goes on to say, "To travel a thousand miles without becoming fatigued, traverse unoccupied terrain."

Often market share is won and lost long before a product is introduced to the marketplace. The strength of a company strategy is better at predetermining success than any particular technology or product. The way ergonomics has recently been emerging and used allows a company to make significant strides in improving product categories, even where human-product interfaces have not been well thought out, or quantitatively evaluated and improved. But as we move closer to the year 2000 and more companies improve the quality of their products, processes, and services, top management will find it necessary to incorporate ergonomics as a companywide philosophy if they truly want to use the full power of ergonomics as a strategic advantage.

The most important aspect of a core strategy is to ensure that you have a valid theory at the center of your business. Drucker (1995) puts forward four of the necessary components of a valid business theory:

1. The assumptions about the business environment, mission, and core competencies must fit reality.

2. The above assumptions must fit each other and be synergistic.

3. The business theory must be known and communicated throughout the organization.

4. The theory of business must be constantly tested and refined.

The ongoing revitalization of your business theory is necessary for survival. When the business climate changes, so must your organization's competencies and mission. An organization must question everything, not to induce fear, but to remain abreast of its place in the world and provide, when necessary, trajectory corrections.

Envisioning Strategic Alliances for Product Development

In chapter 8 we mentioned that the major responsibilities of top management entail vision, inspiration, and leadership. Vision is the most ephemeral, while inspiration is the most ambiguous. Yet management must wield all three of these abilities to achieve a successful outcome. As you formulate and articulate your company's vision, remember that scientific discovery cannot be premeditated, as Dr. Medawar's story about Spain demonstrated. Therefore, it is necessary to envision any and all possible strategic alliances for most of your significant product development efforts, especially from your vendors and knowledge workers. An ergonomics competitive strategy builds an alliance directly with customers by satisfying their need for comfort and the right fit. This alliance can be a kind of customer *comfort cult,* whereby product development strategists have a clear vision of the types of products the company needs to make. Meanwhile, because customers could depend upon innovation with quality, the company would be building a customer *allegiance* that would quickly translate into higher profit margins.

Observing Demographic Trends

I grow old... I grow old...
I shall wear the bottoms of my trousers rolled.
−T.S. ELIOT (1917)

In developing your ergonomic competitive strategy it is important that you cultivate a synergy between the demographic trends of your customer base and the inherent strengths of your organization. As discussed in several places in this book, one of the current demographic trends that will profoundly effect your market, products, and services is the aging of the population. This will dramatically alter what your customers need and want. By 2010, 13 percent of the U.S. population will be over 65. By 2030 the percentage will increase to 20 percent (20 percent in Japan, 22 percent in Canada and France and 26 percent in Germany (see Figure 9-4).

By 2050 between 5 and 10 percent of the U.S. population will be over 85 years old. These customers will be knowledgeable, well educated, and have a great deal of product experience combined with disposable income. Many will be physically challenged. As a group they will not tolerate incomplete or improperly thought-out products or services. They will expect the products to match their capabilities. They will want high quality at a conservative price.

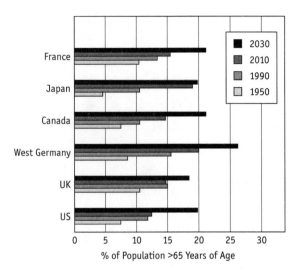

Figure 9-4. Increase in Population of Individuals Over 65 Years of Age

In evaluating products for older individuals several basic research questions come to mind (Laux, 1995):

1. What are the body changes that occur in older individuals and do they differ significantly from younger customers?

2. How do these age-related physiologic or cognitive changes affect older individuals' interactions with products in a safe, productive, and comfortable manner?

3. What product design characteristics support safe, productive, and comfortable functioning?

The answers to these questions require an understanding of the aged and the willingness to objectively evaluate products with older subjects. As we age, a wide range of difficulties emerge (Laux, 1995):

1. 25% of individuals over 65 are visually impaired, and 20% cannot read a newspaper even with their glasses.

2. 30% of individuals over 65 have hearing impairments.

3. 50% of individuals over 65 have arthritis.

4. 8% of individuals over 75 have diabetes.

5. Olfaction, taste, pain, pressure, temperature, and touch sensitivity all decrease with age.

6. Lack of balance is reported by 90% of outpatients in geriatric clinics.

7. Stature and weight both decline gradually with age after 60 years.

8. Osteoarthritis is present in 33% of adults by the time they are 40 and is the leading cause of disability in individuals over 65.

9. Memory shows significant age related changes by age 60.

Many other changes are also the result of aging. The point is that to design products that an aging market purchases and enjoys requires a product development focus that is sensitive to the major demographic factor in modern society—the aging of the population. This means you need a new, additional focus for product design and development that will further differentiate your product from your competitors.

Additionally, as intelligent products begin to proliferate, the aging population will motivate a new industry to develop body replacement and enhancement parts. This industry will be a fusion of microelectronics and molecular biology *(molecular biotronics)*. Micromechanisms, built out of electron-beam machined silicon, are likely to be among the first of this new class of products.

From this point forward, corporate survival and sensibility dictate that products and services must be designed for men and women, young and old, healthy and physically challenged.

ERGONOMICS, CHANGE, AND ETHICS

> Most people live, whether physically, intellectually or morally, in a very restricted circle of their potential being. They make use of a very small portion of their possible consciousness, and of their soul's resources in general, much like a man who, out of his whole bodily organism, should get into a habit of using and moving only his little finger. Great emergencies and crises show us how much greater our vital resources are than we had supposed.
>
> —WILLIAM JAMES TO W. LUTOSLAWSKI, MAY 6, 1906.

Most people are afraid of change. Change means chaos. But chaos can be beautiful in the way it combines both deterministic occurrences with unpredictable events (Wheatley, 1994). This is why it is such a good model for what happens in nature—even human nature and society. The success of the democratic experiment in the United States epitomizes this fact. We have become multifaceted, unique in capabilities and drive. We have a need to create that has been sustained and focused over the years. In this "deterministic" democratic environment, the convergence of an individual's unique capabilities with seemingly random needs and unpredictable events creates the foundation for individual contribution and fulfillment. One can view this convergence as a type of grace for countries—no five-year plans, no ten-year plans, no specific plans at all— just a creative environment where the individual's constant need for inspiration and expression of capabilities can manifest as best they can. An environment that allows for chaos, or change, provides opportunities for people to continuously innovate and develop new concepts, opportunities that are inherent in a free market or laissez-faire environment. When practiced well, ergonomics, working in an environment of constant change and continuous innovation, acts as a Gestalt to remove many of the obstacles that come between people and the tools they need to realize their inspiration and express their capabilities.

Ergonomics also strives to achieve a harmony between dynamism/productivity and safety/comfort. It espouses the best egalitarian ethos combined with a Calvinist desire for ultimate productivity and success. Ergonomics is a set of tools that discriminates between workplaces and products that fit, from those where designers have mismeasured the customer. Ergonomics separates the young and healthy from the aging and physically challenged for the purpose of accommodating all in order to optimize the individual's contribution, safety, and enjoyment. When viewed from a pragmatic corporate sensibility, ergonomics translates directly into improved workplaces, products, process, market share, and profits.

The first obstacle to overcome for the integration of technology and people is the design of the human-product interface. The second obstacle is the strength of the culture in which this integration is taking place. An organization that supports the individual is one that minimizes fear of the unknown. This is not paternalism, like the very good, past days at IBM, but rather, mutual actualization, where enthusiasm for change replaces fear of new technology and leads to potential advantage. Physical and cognitive comfort are antithetical to fear—the comfort to perform, the comfort to enjoy the technological improvements that surround us and our work. Productivity without enjoyment is a form of enslavement—a by-product and Victorian viewpoint well-documented in Charles Dickens' *Hard Times*. It implied that technology's only purpose is to improve the efficiency of human labor at the expense of everything else. What the twenty-first century promises is technologically superior products and services at a lower price, as well as total employee involvement, empowerment, and self-actualization.

Technology is a general category of tools that has taken on an evolutionary proportion in the development of the species. We no longer evolve only biologically, we evolve technologically, which perhaps is an extension of our new-found biology and consciousness. Ergonomics is about taking that technology and balancing it with efficiency and creativity; productivity and safety; as well as satisfaction through personal development. Companies that flourish in this new era of unbounded technology will have genuine respect for the power of the individual and the collective achievement potential of ergonomically empowered souls.

WHAT YOU SHOULD KNOW

1. World class products need to fit the individual, be easy to use, expand the capabilities of the individual, and they must be safe. World class factories will have ergonomic manufacturing workplaces, will design ergonomic products and tools that will, in turn, fabricate other products or provide services.

2. Universities are an unusually good, often untapped source for ergonomic product development alliances.

3. It is important that you keep your development team in touch with each other continuously, even if they are in the same building on different floors.

4. Strategic planning is the most important aspect in guaranteeing success in ergonomic product research and development.

5. To survive and prosper, your organization must become good at forming and navigating strategic alliances. Success is based on leveraging your strengths and making weaknesses irrelevant.

WHAT YOU SHOULD DO

1. Formulate a strategic model or world view.

2. Develop and implement an ergonomic competitive strategy to capture additional market share based on improved product comfort, accommodation, and the creation of customer delight.

3. Develop a synergy between the demographic trends of your customer base and the inherent strengths of your organization.

4. Develop great products for an aging population and/or the physically challenged.

10

companies that have succeeded with EQ

Difficult things beneath heaven are made up of easy
things. Big things beneath heaven are made up
of small things. Thus the sage never deals
with the great, but accomplishes greatness.

—LAO-TSU (604-531 BC)

BLACK & DECKER

When Black & Decker wanted to increase their market share of cordless professional drills in their top-of-the-line DeWalt tool division, they turned to the ergonomic best-in-class analysis. Black & Decker has long been an innovator in the design and production of power tools, appliances, and accessories. However, in recent years the number and quality of competitors had increased to the point of negatively impacting market share. The U.S. power tool group took an aggressive position: "develop the highest performance, most ergonomically correct cordless professional drill."

From the very beginning ergonomics was an integral part of the new product development process. After the best-in-class assessment was performed to determine the strengths and weakness of existing cordless drill designs, a group of experienced drill users was asked to use a wide variety of in-house prototypes as well as products from competitors. Wrist stress, vibration, joint angles, and skin pressure were measured while performing several typical drilling tasks. Additionally, we calculated the approximate location of the center-of-mass of the drill with respect to the center-of-mass of the hand to determine the kind of torque the drill placed upon each user's wrist. Comfort assessments indicated the need to change the geometry of the trigger and handle to reduce the torque on the wrist.

The difference between a good drill and a great drill can be measured in millimeters. Subtle changes in the design can translate into significant improvements in user comfort over the course of the day. As a result of having achieved the goal for performance and total ergonomic quality, the new cordless professional drill line has achieved remarkable sales across several SKUs and garnered significant market share gains against other tool competitors. (SKUs are itemized numbers used to identify products for ordering and inventory.) Sales volume was three times the projected amount, and during the first two years they couldn't produce them fast enough. The product has won numerous awards including the gold medal from *BusinessWeek* for successful design. Black & Decker 's experience with this product inspired them to establish their own in-house ergonomics laboratory. Ergonomic principles are now an integral part of the design process at Black & Decker.

KNOLL

Knoll set the goal of building the world's most comfortable office chair for the vast number of mid-market and growth companies. To achieve this goal the product development and marketing team needed to produce a chair that had a list price that was $200 less than the leading office chairs on the market. Using concurrent engineering and guided by the ergonomic best-in-class analysis process, Knoll created the Parachute office chair. A first step in this process was to evaluate several prototype chairs against the best selling chairs in the office furniture market. An integral part of the ergonomic best-in-class analysis was to determine the seat comfort for each chair tested. To accomplish this, load distribution patterns were measured for each chair using a seat pressure assessment system. While sitting in the chairs, all subjects performed typical office tasks such as entering data into a computer. A wide variety of subjects were used to ensure that pressure distributions would be representative of a wide range of body types. Simultaneously, user-comfort preferences were recorded with a series of questionnaires. Additionally, typing accuracy and speed were measured. The ergonomic best-in-class analysis documented which chairs and prototypes were most comfortable. Perhaps most importantly, they got valuable information as to why certain chairs were more comfortable than others.

This information was then used to make recommendations for seat and back contours, as well as the range and type of adjustability for the seat and backrest. All of these assessments were performed on-line, as part of the concurrent engineering process. Ergonomic recommendations were fed back to the design team, whereupon digital prototypes and physical mock-ups were made for further assessments. In about eight months, the result was a line of office chairs that were significantly more comfortable and less expensive than the world's best selling office chairs. But Knoll didn't stop here. When the product line was launched, ergonomics fitted prominently into the sales and marketing program. Literature was produced that described the amount of measurement and attention that went into designing comfort into the chair. A video was produced that featured interviews with the entire development team including the sales professionals. The marketplace acceptance and sales of the new chair line have been extraordinary.

COOPER POWER TOOLS

When Cooper Power Tools, one of the largest tool companies in the U.S., decided to increase their sales to Boing by developing a new line of pneumatic drills that were more powerful, yet minimized wrist stress, they turned to the ergonomic best-in-class process. Pneumatic drills from the best manufacturers in the world were assembled for the test. Experienced users were asked to try out and rate each of the tools. Wrist posture and finger pressure during tool use was measured as was vibration transmission through the hand and muscle activity. The best-in-class analysis yielded several interesting facts:

1. The handle shape on most pneumatic drills is backwards, that is, the handle increases in diameter as you descend the handle.

2. Pneumatic drill users prefer to hold the drill handle in different positions as a function of the force they need to exert on the handle.

3. Due the drill's pronounced extension from the handle, the trigger switch on many drills increases the amount of force with which the muscles have to contract.

4. A handle of only one size would have a difficult time fitting a large percentage of the population comfortably.

All of these issues were addressed simply by changing the geometry of the housing. To further increase user comfort, the inner surfaces of the drills were coated to reduce cold conduction through the handle (pneumatic tools are in fact heat exchangers that drop in temperature as a function of the work performed by the motor).

The result was the development of the most comfortable pneumatic drill on the market. Cooper Power Tools took the additional step of making the tool in two sizes to better accommodate female users of their product. Better fit and enhanced comfort were the result. The bottom line was increased drill sales and customer delight. Cooper Power Tools has since expanded their ergonomic line to include grinders, snipers, and other tools and is now recognized as one of the world leaders in ergonomic pneumatic tools.

LOGITECH

Logitech is one of the best peripheral input device manufacturers in the world. They specialize in designing and producing high quality computer mice that are reliable, accurate, and competitively priced. Several years ago, in an effort to improve customer comfort while using a mouse, they embarked on a program to develop the world's first ergonomically designed mouse.

The challenge for the Logitech development team was to measure the effect of using a mouse on user accuracy, comfort, and speed. A video game was devised, whereupon subjects were asked to navigate through a maze using different types of mice. To record the user's accuracy, the number of times the cursor collided with the walls of the maze was monitored. Simultaneously, the muscle activity of the subject's forearm flexors and extensors was recorded along with multiple video views of the mouse user's dominant hand. Additionally, the subject's comfort level was recorded using questionnaires during the performance of all mouse tracking trials. The results of these tests made it amazingly clear that the mouse with the slanted asymmetrical surface was easier to use (required less muscle effort) as it minimized the amount of *pronation* of the forearm during mouse-intensive tasks, making it a more natural, biomechanical extension of the hand.

In conjunction with their new, ergonomically designed mouse, the company embarked on a marketing program to educate their customers on the benefits of ergonomics, including the need for left- and right-handed mice. Customer response has been tremendously positive, making Logitech's ergonomic mouse an unbelievable marketplace success.

PERFECT FIT, INDUSTRIES, INC.

When Perfect Fit, Industries, Inc., a division of Foamex International, Inc., wanted to introduce a line of pillows that would increase global customer fit and comfort, they used a biomechanically based assessment process. Perfect Fit requested that each pillow be evaluated to determine the specific size accommodations necessary for every body type. Using three-dimensional human-computer-aided design, digital mannequins from different populations were evaluated with digital mock-ups of the pillows. When potential problems of fit were identified, design recommendations were presented to the Perfect Fit development team. These recommendations were then incorporated into new prototypes for testing. Prior to launch, the company developed and included ergonomics information along with the retail packaging for the pillows. The result was the successful introduction of a new line of comfort pillows that take on a new dimension for pillows because they are shaped to fit the full range of human body sizes.

LONG ISLAND LIGHTING COMPANY (LILCO)

The application of quantitative ergonomics to the gas and electric utility industry was nearly uncharted even as recently as 1992. In 1993, the Long Island Lighting Company (LILCO), one of the largest utilities in the U.S., set out to change all of that. They reasoned that both safety and employee morale could be potentially improved through the implementation of an ergonomics program focused on back and wrist injuries. LILCO, through their research and development initiative program, engaged an ergonomics specialist to do design and implement a work-place assessment program for the gas division. The workplace environment, work methods, and tools were all analyzed with the goal to optimize ease of use and reduce musculoskeletal stressors. In a sense, this was ergonomics on the go, as most measures were made in the field, where the work was performed.

Many traditional tools and work methods were scrutinized with quantifiable biomechanical assessments. Ergonomists followed the work teams in trenches while they were laying and repairing gas pipe. Digitized, sequential video images were then fed into a 3-D biomechan-ical model to determine joint force and injury potential. Muscle activity was measured with portable EMG systems and force gauges were used to determine the magnitude of forces applied by the hands to a wide variety of handheld tools. Additionally, vibration transmitted through the hands from pneumatic tools was measured and compared to ISO standards for exposure.

Numerous recommendations were made from the redesign of the Jack Hammer™ to the use of antivibration gloves. From a business per-spective, the quantitative assessments provided the objective rationale needed by management to warrant the implementation of numerous stress reduction strategies. To further support and help implement these recommendations, the ergonomists also suggested that other depart-ments be included in LILCO's research and development initiative program. So the Strong Internal Support Team was set up. This task force included employees from the research and development initiative program, medical services, corporate safety, and gas design and construction. The last group included employees who actually worked in the field.

LILCO, operating under a continuous improvement model, is now systematically implementing ergonomic changes to equipment and tools, work methods, and training programs. For an ergonomics program to be completely successful it is important that all three of these things are implemented. LILCO estimates it will take approximately three years to implement all of the recommendations, and the anticipated return on investment for the next ten years is 9:1.

At LILCO, ergonomics has become a vehicle to help management channel the innovative capacity of LILCO's diversified employee base to improve safety and productivity. This is a valuable by-product of an ergonomics program when applied to a mature industry like gas and electric utilities. For Long Island Lighting Company, ergonomics has become a practical, low-cost tool for reducing injuries and their associated costs.

CNA RISK MANAGEMENT GROUP

CNA is a major insurance company in North America that utilizes workplace ergonomics as a risk management strategy to reduce musculoskeletal injury claims and cost. As part of their total quality program to enhance customer service they created an ergonomics service group. CNA ergonomic specialists visit customer facilities to make recommendations for workplace improvement.

During one of the many on-site workplace assessments, CNA visited a unionized workplace with a large number of reported injuries. For the most difficult jobs assessed, recommendations of work rotation were made to distribute these larger forces over a group of individuals to lessen their cumulative effect to only a few workers (a risk distribution approach to ergonomics). However, current union rules would not allow such a program to be implemented. CNA persuaded the company and the union to try the job rotation schedule for two weeks. Absenteeism on these jobs was dramatically reduced and subsequently the recommendation was permanently adopted. Job rotation can be a low-cost strategy for reducing musculoskeletal injuries and empowering other efficiency gains.

In CNA's experience, back injuries can cost anywhere from $100 to $300,000 with $9,000 as the average, and most large companies of 1,000 or more employees have at least 100 back injuries a year. As a result of their objective data collection, CNA is in the unique position of inspiring their customers with an accurate estimate of the cost of inaction. For example, a simple recommendation for purchasing a spring load table costing about $5,000 would reduce the frequency with which people have to perform lifting motions. This in turn would cut down on the number of back injuries. By preventing just one back injury the spring load table pays for itself.

CNA also provides consulting services and training for employees and managers on ergonomic concerns and awareness. CNA feels it is important to educate employees about improved workstations and how they impact their quality of life. Technical training is provided to instruct employees in the use of new equipment to best perform a task with minimal injury potential.

CNA is discovering that companies who implement ergonomic programs are, in addition to reducing cumulative trauma disorders, improving productivity, product quality, and employee morale. In today's highly competitive insurance marketplace, quality-conscious, full-service providers like CNA are combining ergonomics and continuous improvement to reduce claims costs and premiums for their accounts.

DUPONT

DuPont is a good example of a company that aggressively pursues business development and safety. In its early days as a manufacturer of explosives (1802), the companyís founder had a wise approach towards safety and occupational accidents. In fact, he built one of his homes adjacent to a gunpowder factory to underscore the commitment to safety. The current CEO of DuPont requires that all lost-time injuries be reported in writing to him within twenty-four hours. As a result of these efforts, DuPont's injury rates are about 1/5 of the industry norms; a number of facilities have not lost workdays due to injuries for several years. One of DuPont's plants in Tennessee holds the National Safety Council (NSC) record for the most continuous days without an injury (almost seven years) (Reder, 1995). So successful are DuPont's safety efforts that they have formed an organization to market their internal safety services to other companies. The group is called Safety and Environmental Management Services.

When DuPont asked our ergonomic team to develop a back injury program for the company their back injury experience was similar to other companies in the U.S. For DuPont, however, this was unacceptable, especially in light of their excellent results in preventing instantaneous traumatogenic injuries. Our team was charged with implementing a global ergonomics training program in five countries (United States, Switzerland, Mexico, Japan, and Brazil). The goal was to develop a *Back Injury Prevention Program* by training managers, engineers, and safety specialist in the techniques for quantitatively evaluating workplace jobs and developing practical engineering and training solutions to reduce pain and discomfort. Our primary tool to evaluate workplace jobs was biomechanical software that simulated worker movement and estimated body joint forces. We then compared these forces with acceptable strengths in the population to determine if a job would exceed an individual's capabilities. We also trained participants in the development of intervention strategies for reducing work stressors that contribute to back injuries. Materials were developed in five languages to augment the software and training manuals.

The instructional materials included four volumes on the biome-chanics and ergonomics of workplace injuries. Included in the material were over 5,090 slides to facilitate the sharing of the concepts in an eas-ily understood manner. PC-based software was developed for the design engineers. This included biomechanical models for evaluating body forces and determining the percent of a population capable of perform-ing a task dynamically along with a global anthropometric database of the sizes and strengths of people worldwide. Further, a real-time, audi-ble biofeedback monitor was developed to provide feedback on muscle contraction during the performance of workplace tasks. This tool was developed to provide the production engineers with a way to determine whether a particular design was likely to increase muscle force require-ments. Now, the real challenge was to develop an effective, three-day training program that could be taken on the road to training centers in five countries. To help transcend the potential language barrier with regard to technical terms, a six-language ergonomics and technical term glossary was developed in English, Japanese, French, German, Spanish, and Portuguese. Along with this effort, the information was simultane-ously translated in Japan to help improve the training efficacy.

DuPont then needed to have the CEO and Board visibly support the program for it to be introduced into the corporate culture. To this end, the CEO wrote a beautifully inspiring letter that went out to all managers in an attempt to focus the team on the impending program. Training was divided between theoretical information and practical hands-on case studies in a computer lab. All participants were tested before and after program implementation. Standard evaluation forms were utilized to evaluate speaker competence and material relevance.

When a large training effort works, the energy that develops is con-tagious and spreads out among all of the participants. Even across language and cultural barriers, the strong idea that it is possible to reduce musculoskeletal injuries to the spine through biomechanical workplace measurement of jobs and tasks took root. DuPont was simply not going to diminish its sterling reputation as a leader in safety.

The result of the program was unbelievable. From the time the CEO wrote the supporting letter to participants, to one year following implementation of the program to reduce costs related to back injury, DuPont saved more than 10 million dollars as a result of preventing back injuries. This savings translates into a yearly earnings improvement of two cents per share. At DuPont, with a price/earnings (stock price as a multiple of earnings) of 14, this might translate into 28 cents per share price, or a market capitalization increase of $155,000,000 in one year, as a result of preventing back injuries. Another major by-product of the program was the implementation of an in-house ergonomics program. DuPont is now considered to be a leader in ergonomics in the chemical industry.

These are but a few of the companies already using ergonomic quality as a tool to satisfy their customers through improved comfort and fit. The result is often substantial gains in market share and profitability. I encourage all companies that make products and provide services to experience the immense satisfaction that results from producing ergonomically superior products and workplaces.

appendix

The Center for Product Ergonomics (CPE) at the University of South Florida is the first U.S. university center focused on applying biomechanically based ergonomics to product design. The mission of the center is to develop and apply new ergonomics technology to measure and improve the interface between people and products. Its focus is to empower the physically disabled and the elderly to achieve performance parity in the workplace and the home through ergonomically superior product designs.

The Center is comprised of ergonomic experts, physicians, and scientists from the College of Public Health at the University of South Florida. The Center operates a state-of-the-art product ergonomics laboratory for the quantitative evaluation of the effect of product design on customer performance. With their unique combination of technologies they are able to rapidly measure body stress under realistic product-use scenarios. This allows for an objective ergonomics best-in-class comparison of products. From these assessments, CPE scientists can then develop practical solutions to improve the comfort, ease-of-use, and performance of consumer products.

For more information contact:

Center for Product Ergonomics
College of Public Health
University of South Florida
13201 Bruce B. Downs Blvd.
Tampa, Florida 33612
Tel 813-974-6668
Fax 813-974-4718
E Mail cgross@koop.coph.usf.edu

glossary

Acetylcholine (ACh): body chemical that helps in transmitting nerve impulses.

Adenosine triphosphate (ATP): an ester of adenosine and triphosphoric

Ambiguity: the condition of admitting of two or more meanings. In the case of management, the ability to handle the interplay or tension that may result from opposition or contraposing of apparently incompatible or contradictory elements or levels of meaning. (see uncertainty)

Analog: of, related to, or being a mechanism in which data is represented by continuously variable physical quantities.

Andenosine: a nucleoside that is a constituent of RNA yielding adenine and ribose on hydrolysis.

Anthropometry: measures human physical dimensions (e.g., eye height, leg length) and functional characterizations (such as reach) to determine differences between individuals and groups. **Anthropometrics** refers specifically to the design and evaluation of products and workplaces.

Applied ergonomics: the practical use of ergonomic principles to solve product and workplace problems.

Biomechanical modeling: mathematical models of body function used to predict how the body will respond under a given set of conditions.

Biomechanics: in ergonomics, the field that studies classical mechanical principles and their relationships as used by or applied to living organisms or biological tissues.

Body position (posture): a qualitative description of the general position of the body (i.e., standing, sitting).

Carpal Tunnel Syndrome (CTS): a potentially painful disability in which the manipulative or gripping abilities of the hand and fingers are reduced due to median nerve compression injury within the carpal tunnel.

Comfort: in ergonomics, the qualitative description of a user's state of subjective well-being in relation to their external environment; the absence of significant or excessive physical and/or mental stressors.

Comfort cult: an ergonomics competitive strategy that builds an alliance directly with customers by satisfying their need for comfort and the right fit.

Compensation: a movement of a part of the body to restore or maintain equilibrium as another body part moves.

Continuous improvement: the Japanese term is kaizen. A continuous incremental improvement process that involves everyone—managers and workers alike.

Continuous innovation: achieved by combining or integrating product innovation and process innovation (continuous improvement).

Coxal bone: the bone cavity near the hip joint.

Cumulative musculoskeletal injury: injuries that are the result of repetitive, forceful responses to physical requirements.

Cumulative Trauma Disorder (CTD): a breakdown of a body part as a result of repetitive overuse, overexertion, or excessive stress.

Delivery of ergonomic services: a new system of creating wealth that results from adding ergonomic-based services to the primary products that come from agriculture, manufacturing, mining, and fuel. In ergonomics, the goal is to create a transparent interface between the consumer and these hybrid products/services.

Digital measurement: discrete computer-based numerical measurements.

Dose-response relationship: the association between a given exposure and the outcome which results form this exposure.

Dosimeter: an instrument or device that measures body exposure to a wide range of agents.

Effort: the expenditure of physical and/or mental energy in the performance of some task.

Electromyography (EMG): the study, measurement, recording, analysis, and/or interpretation of the electrical activity of muscles.

Erector spinae muscles: the long muscles of the back that help extend the spinal column.

Ergonomic aesthetic: strategy for a development team to create product uniqueness by using a creative process that makes an imaginative and technological leap beyond objective product functionality. Contemplating the attributes that create product aesthetics.

Ergonomic assessment: the detailed analysis of a product's ergonomic features, i.e., the results of an ergonomic best-in-class analysis.

Ergonomic best-in-class analysis: a process for evaluating the quality of the interface between the user and a class of product.

Ergonomic push products: type of product that is based on optimizing user comfort and fit. The comfort and fit then drives these products into the marketplace.

Ergonomic quality (EQ): the systematic approach to bringing biome-chanically-based ergonomics into the manufacturing process.

Ergonomics: the creation of transparent interfaces between people and products. Research mainly involves studying human psychological, social, physical, and biological characteristics, maintaining the infor-mation obtained from that research, and working to apply that information with respect to the design, operation, or use of products or systems for optimizing human performance, health, safety, efficiency, and/or habitability.

Etiology: the branch of medical science concerned with the cause and origin of disease.

Exoskeletal products: products that more fully empower the human body by being designed as extensions of the human body.

Extensor: any muscle whose contraction normally causes joint extension.

Flexor: any muscle that flexes a joint.

Fovea: a depressed region within the macula lutea of the posterior retina at which cone density is highest and greatest visual acuity occurs.

Frequency distribution: the number of instances obtained or the probability of the occurrence of a score for a given variable value.

Gestalt psychology: school of psychology that deals mainly with the processes of perception. According to Gestalt psychology, images are perceived as a pattern or a whole rather than merely as a sum of distinct component parts.

Human-computer-aided design: the next generation of computer-aided design (CAD) software. Can simulate the postures and movements of customers as they use a product.

In vivo: within a living organism.

Instantaneous traumatogenic injuries: injuries that occur immediately following exposure, i.e., fracture of wrist after falling on hand.

Ischial tuberosity: a projection at the base of the ischium that can produce a pressure point when sitting on a surface.

Ischium: the inferior and posterior portion of each coxal bone.

Isokinetic: constant speed of motion.

Iteration: a computational procedure in which replication of a cycle of operations produces results which approximate the desired result more and more closely.

Kaizen: means continuous incremental improvement. When applied to the workplace kaizen means a group-oriented continuous improvement process involving everyone—managers and workers alike. The main orientation is on the person-process for improvement.

Leverage: to increase mechanical or strategic advantage.

Likert scales: scales that numerically rate and combine responses to a user's perceptions.

Loads (external): the strain that is placed on the body from lifting, pulling, carrying, etc.

Microcosm: denotes a conception of a human being as a complete world, universe, or cosmos in miniature within ourselves. A little world.

Mitochondria: any of various round or long cellular organelles that are found outside the nucleus, produce energy for the cell through cellular respiration, and are rich in fats, proteins, and enzymes.

Multiple analysis of variance: a statistical technique for evaluating the difference between data sets containing multiple dimensions.

Multiple and partial correlation: a statistical technique for evaluating the strength of the relationship between multiple data sets.

Multiple regression analysis: the analysis or use of the combined and individual contributions form more than one predictor variable for predicting the value of a single criterion variable.

Musculoskeletal injury: an injury to the muscles, bones, joints, and associated soft tissues in the body.

Musculoskeletal system: the integrated system of muscles, bones, joints, and associated soft tissues in the body.

Mutual actualization: to bring two or more people into a more meaningful level of existence and action.

Myogenic: originating in muscle as an impulse.

Myogenesis: muscle growth.

Nanometer: one billionth of a meter. **Nanosecond** is one billionth of a second.

Neuromuscular junction: that point of interface between the motor neuron and muscle tissue at which the synapse occurs.

Neurotransmitter: a chemical released from one neuron at a chemical synapse for which a receptor is located nearby on the same or another neuron.

Newton: an SI unit of force. A small English apple weighs about 1 Newton.

Nicotinamide Adenine Dinucleotide Phosphate (NADH): a compound of the vitamin B complex found especially as a constituent of coenzymes and used similarly to nicotinic acid (niacin). Nicotinic acid is an acid of the vitamin B complex found widely in animals and plants and used especially against pellagra (also called niacin).

Nonparametric statistics: any statistical analysis which makes no assumption about the population distribution.

Occupational biomechanics: the study of the volitional acts of the individual in loading the musculoskeletal system in the working environment.

Orthogonal: having perpendicular slope or tangents at the points of intersection; having a sum of products or an integral that is zero or sometimes under specified conditions. For instance, real-valued functions, vectors, a square matrix, and a linear transformation.

Parameter: an arbitrarily defined constant value under a given set of circumstances from which other values or functions may be defined.

Parametric statistics: those statistical analyses that assume a known, typically a normally-distributed, population.

Pneumatic: adapted for holding or inflated with compressed air.

Popliteal crease: body joint at the back of the knee.

Pressure point: a location of concentrated load on the body.

Process improvement: generic method for systematically enhancing the quality of a product or service.

Product differentiation: an important part of ergonomic strategic planning for product development that seeks to provide product lines with a distinct competitive advantage by creating the right fit between the product(s) and customer, as well as meeting and exceeding the ever changing needs and demands of the marketplace.

Product improvement: improves the process (process improvement) resulting in greater efficiency and less injuries.

Product iterations: the number of times a product has to be replicated or fabricated before it approximates the desired result.

Proprioceptive: of, relating to, or being stimuli that arise within the organism.

Proprioceptive activity: regarding measuring the skin; skin pressure feedback.

Proprioceptive feedback: regarding the muscle activity of the user and a product; an external switch that informs the user of the product that an activation has occurred.

Prototype: a model of the preliminary version of a product that is produced prior to fabrication of the production item and is representative of the final system for testing and evaluation.

Psychometric: the measurement of psychological processes that use experimental design and statistical techniques.

Quality function deployment (QFD): the voice of the customer in product development.

Radial deviation: a movement of the wrist such that the longitudinal axis of the hand is directed toward the lateral/radial/thumb side of the forearm.

Self-actualization: bringing the self into a more meaningful level of existence.

Somatic resonance: moving in tune with the body.

Stressors: physical and psychological agents that may contribute to or produce an untoward response in an organism.

Subjective correlates: physical variables that have a defined relationship to expressed personal feelings.

Synergy: a condition in which the interaction of two or more agents or systems produces an effect that may be greater than the effect produced by equal amounts or efforts of the individual agents or systems acting separately.

Torque: the effective perpendicular component of a force (or the effective sum of forces) applied to an object some distance from a point representing an axis about which rotation can occur, inducing or tending to induce an angular acceleration.

Toxic agents: those substances that can cause harm when overly exposed to the body. In the case of musculoskeletal injury, the toxic agent is produced by the body itself under specific workplace conditions and requirements.

Transparent interface: the invisible boundary between people and products.

Ulnar deviation: a movement or position of the longitudinal axis of the hand toward the ulnar/little finger side of the forearm.

Uncertainty: in management, to be able to reason, deal with, or listen to something that is doubtful, unknown, or not capable of being readily demonstrated to you (see ambiguity).

Uncertainty principle: the act of observation affects what one is attempting to measure. A principle in quantum mechanics that states it is impossible to assert in ordinary conventional terms what the specified point of a particle (e.g., an electron) is and at the same time identify its specified momentum.

Variance: a measure of the dispersion about the mean of a distribution, represented by the second moment of the deviations from a mean value in normally distributed population.

Velocity: in ergonomics, a vector that represents the rate of change of position or displacement of an object with time.

Work stressors: physical and psychological agents found in the workplace which may contribute to or produce an untoward response in an individual.

bibliography

Asmussen, E. "Growth in Muscular Strength and Power." *Physical Activity, Human Growth, and Development* (edited by G.L. Ranick). New York: Academic Press, 1973.

Barker, J.A. *Paradigms.* New York: Harper Collins, 1992.

Bejjanni, F. and Landsmeer, J. "Biomechanics of the Hand." *Basic Biomechanics of The Musculoskeletal System* (edited by M. Nordin and V.H. Frankel). Philadelphia: Lea & Febiger, 1989.

Besterfield, D.H., C. Besterfield-Michna, G.H. Besterfield, and M. Besterfield-Sacre. *Total Quality Management.* Englewood Cliffs, New Jersey: Prentice Hall, 1995.

Bhote, Keki R. *World Class Quality.* New York: American Management Association, 1991.

Bralla, James G. *Design for Excellence.* New York: McGraw-Hill, 1996.

Burenhult, G., ed. *The First Humans.* New York: Harper Collins, 1993.

Chaffin, D.B., and K.S. Park. "A Longitudinal Study of Low Back Pain as Associated with Occupational Lifting Factors." *American Industrial Hygiene Association Journal* 34 (1973): 513-525.

Chapanis, A. "Ergonomics in Product Development: A Personal View." *Ergonomics* 38, no. 8 (1995): 1625-1638.

Clifton, D.O., and P. Nelson. *Soar With Your Strengths.* New York: Delacorte Press, 1992.

Cohen, L. *Quality Function Deployment.* New York: Addison-Wesley Publishing Company, 1995.

Dalfonso, M.A. *ISO 9000: Achieving Compliance and Certification.* New York: John Wiley and Sons, 1995.

Deming, W. Edwards. *The New Economics*. Cambridge, Mass.: Massachusetts Institute of Technology, Center for Advanced Engineering Study, 1994.

Drucker, P.F. *The New Realities*. New York: Harper Collins, 1989.

Drucker, P.F. *Management in a Time of Great Change*. New York: Truman Talley Books, 1995.

DuPree, M. *Leadership is an Art*. New York: Dell Publishing, 1989.

Elstrom, P. "The Next Era: Humanizing of Technology." *Investor's Business Daily* (Monday, October 9, 1995): A8.

Emerson, R. W. "The Conduct of Life." *Selected Essays, Fate,1860*. New York: Viking Penguin Books, 1982.

Families and Work Institute. "The Changing Workforce." *The Practical Guide to Practically Everything*. (P. Bernstein and C. Ma). New York: Random House Publishing, 1995.

Grandjean, E. *Fitting the Tasks to the Man*, 4th ed. New York: Taylor and Francis, 1995.

Gross, C. "Using Ergonomics to Prevent Back Injuries." *Corporate Fitness and Recreation* 4, no. 3 (April 1985).

Gross, C. "An Ergonomic Approach to Managing Carpal Tunnel Syndrome." *Industrial Safety and Hygiene News* (October 1985).

Gross, C., R. Andree, and E. Chapnik. *Frequency of Lift and Back Pain Among Patient Handlers*. 39th ACEMB, Omni International Hotel, Baltimore, Maryland. September 1986.

Gross, C., and E. Chapnik. "Visual Display Terminals: Health Issues And Productivity." *Personnel* (May 1987).

Gross, C., and S. Wang. *Carpal Tunnel Syndrome: A Review of the Literature*. Proceedings of the Mid-Central Ergonomics/Human Factors meeting, University of Illinois at Urbana-Champaign, Illinois. July 16, 1987.

Gross, C., K. Costello, L. Mikulionis, and D. Glossop. *Biomechanical Assessment of Automotive Ingress/Egress.* Proceedings of the Mid-Central Ergonomics/Human Factors meeting, University of Illinois at Urbana-Champaign, Illinois. July 16, 1987.

Gross, C., and E. Chapnik. "Evaluation: Office Improvements Can Reduce VDT Operator Problems." *Occupational Health & Safety* (July 1987).

Gross, C. "Ergonomic Workplace Assessments are the First Step in Injury Treatment." *Occupational Health & Safety* (May 1988).

Gross, C. "Ergonomic Aspects of Computer Terminal Operations." (chapter) *Success Factors for Implementing Change: A Manufacturing Viewpoint.* Society of Manufacturing Engineers, 1989.

Gross, C., and A. Fuchs. "Ergonomics Programs Reduce Costly Workplace Injuries." *Occupational Health & Safety* (January 1990).

Gross, C. "Mannequin: Human-Computer-Aided Design." Cseriac *Gateway* 2: no. 4 (Fall 1991): 11-14.

Gross, C., and C. Hassel. "Ergonomics: Making Life Easier And Safer For Computer Users." *Computer Digest* (November 1991).

Gross, C., R. Goonetilleke, K. Menon, J. Banaag, and C. Nair. "Biomechanical Assessment And Prediction of Seat Comfort." *Automotive Technology International '92* (December 1991).

Gross, C. "Occupational Biomechanics: Preventing Musculoskeletal Injuries in the Workplace." *Engineering Division News.* American Society of Safety Engineers, Spring 1992.

Gross, C. "A Biomechanical Approach to Ergonomic Product Design." (chapter) *Maynards Industrial Engineering Handbook,* 4th ed. New York: McGraw-Hill, 1992.

Gross, C., J. Banaag, R.S. Goonetilleke, and K.K. Menon. "Manufacturing Ergonomics." (chapter) *Maynards Industrial Engineering Handbook,* 4th edition. New York: McGraw-Hill, 1992.

Gross, C., G. Krueger, H. Lu, and J. Jarvinen. "A New Approach to Performing Ergonomic Workplace Assessments." *Workplace Ergonomics Magazine* (March 1995).

Grossmith, E.J. "Product Design Considerations for the Reduction of Ergonomically Related Manufacturing Costs." *Design for Manufacturability: A System Approach to Concurrent Engineering and Ergonomics* (Hellender, M., and N. Nagamichi). Bristol, Penn: Taylor and Francis, Ltd.,1992.

Gruber, H. *Aspects of Scientific Theory: Aesthetics and Cognition in Creativity* (John Brockman, ed.). New York: Simon & Schuster, 1993.

Hartley, John R. *Concurrent Engineering: Shortening Lead Times, Raising Quality, and Lowering Costs.* Portland, Ore.: Productivity Press, 1992.

Helander, M. *A Guide to the Ergonomics of Manufacturing.* Bristol, Penn: Taylor and Francis, Ltd., 1995.

Hettinger, T. "Muskelkraft bei Mannern und Frauen." *Zentralblatt Arbeit und Wissenschaft* 14,(1960): 79-84.

Hoffman, G.M. *The Technology Payoff.* Burr Ridge, Illinois: Irwin Professional Publishing, 1994.

Hoover, G., A. Cambell, and P. Spain. *Hoover's Handbook of American Business 1995.* Austin, Texas: The Reference Press, in association with Warner Books, 1995.

Hunger, J.D., and T.L. Wheelen. *Strategic Management.* Reading, Mass: Addison-Wesley, 1996.

Imai, Masaaki. *Kaizen.* New York: Random House Publishing, 1986.

Kapandji, I.A. *The Physiology of the Joints.* New York: Churchill Livingstone, 1974.

Kuhn, T.S. *The Structure of Scientific Revolutions.* Chicago: The University of Chicago Press, 1970.

Kuorinak, I., and L. Forcier, eds., *Work Related Musculoskeletal Disorders (WMSD's).* Bristol, Penn: Taylor and Francis, Ltd., 1995.

Laurel, B. "Virtual Reality." *Scientific American* (September 1995): 90.

Laux, L., "Aging Techniques." *Research Techniques in Human Engineering*, (J. Weimer). Englewood Cliffs, N.J.: Prentice-Hall, 1995.

Lieber, R.L. *Skeletal Muscle Structure and Function*. Baltimore, Maryland: Williams and Wilkins, 1992.

Lifshitz, Y. and T. Armstrong. *A Design Checklist for Control and Prediction of Cumulative Trauma Disorders in Hand-Intensive Manual Jobs*. Proceedings of the 30th Annual Meeting of Human Factors Society, 1986.

MacLeod, D. *The Ergonomics Edge*. New York: Van Nostrand Reinhold, 1995.

Marras, W. S. "Towards an Understanding of Dynamic Variables in Ergonomics: Low-Back Pain, Carpal Tunnel Syndrome and Upper Extremity Disorders in the Workplace" (editors, J. S. Moore and A. Garg). *State of the Art Reviews, Occupational Medicine* 7, no. 4 (October-December, 1992).

McCarthy, R.L., and T.J. Ayres, C.T. Wood, and J.N. Robinson. "Risk and Effectiveness Criteria for Using On-Product Warnings." *Ergonomics* 38, no. 11 (1995).

McRae, H., *The World in 2020*. Boston, MA: Harvard Business School Press, 1994.

Mears, P. *Quality Improvement Tools and Techniques*. New York: McGraw-Hill, Inc., 1995.

Messadie, G., *Great Scientific Discoveries*. New York: W. & R. Chambers, 1991.

Miller, E., A. Loughlin, E. Nudelman, and D. Thomas. *Future Vision*. Naperville, Illinois: Sourcebooks Trade, 1991.

Minkin, B.H. *Future in Sight*. New York: Macmillan, 1995.

Myers, B. S. and T. Copplestone. *The History of Art*. New York: Dorset Press, 1985.

New, Shirley A. *NIOSH Case Studies in Ergonomics*. Rockville, Maryland: Government Institute, Inc., 1996.

Ng, D., T. Cassar, and C. Gross. "Evaluation of an Intelligent Seat System." *Applied Ergonomics* 26, no. 2 (April 1995).

Noone, D.J. *Creative Problem Solving.* New York: Barron's Educational Services, Hauppauge, 1993.

Nordin M., and V.H. Frankel. *Basic Biomechanics of the Musculoskeletal System.* Philadelphia: Lea and Febiger, 1989.

Patterson, D. "Microprocessors in 2020." *Scientific American* (September 1995): 62.

Pitman, M., and L. Peterson. "Biomechanics of Skeletal Muscle." *Basic Biomechanics of the Musculoskeletal System* (edited by M. Norden and V.H. Frankel). Philadelphia: Lea and Febiger, 1989.

Putz-Anderson, V. *Cumulative Trauma Disorders.* Bristol, Penn: Taylor and Francis, Ltd., 1994.

Reder, A. *75 Best Business Practices for Socially Responsible Companies.* New York: G.T. Putnam's Sons, 1995.

Robinson, Alan, ed. *Continuous Improvement in Operations: A Systematic Approach to Waste Reduction.* Portland, Ore.: Productivity Press, 1991

Schneid, T. D., *The Americans with Disabilities Act.* New York: Van Nostrand Reinhold, 1992.

Shiba, Shoji, Alan Graham, and David Walden. *A New American TQM: Four Practical Revolutions in Management.* Portland, Ore.: Productivity Press, 1993.

Smith, P.G., and D.G. Reinertsen. *Developing Products in Half the Time.* New York: Van Nostrand Reinhold, 1991.

Stamp, Daniel. *The Invisible Assembly Line.* New York: American Management Association, 1995.

Sun-tzu. *The Art of War,* translated by R.D. Sawyer. Boulder, CO.: Westview Press, 1994.

Tichauer, E. *The Biomechanical Basis of Ergonomics.* New York: John Wiley and Sons, 1978.

Todorov, Branimir. *ISO 9000 Required: Your Worldwide Passport to Customer Confidence.* Portland, Ore.: Productivity Press, 1996.

Udo, H., A. Seo, F. Yoshinaga, N.Kurumanti, A. Hisashige, S. Koda, T. Fujimura, Y. Matsumra, K. Matsumra, M. Dejima, M. Iki, A. Udo, and A. Kataoka. "The Effect of a Pelvic Belt on the Incidence of Low Back Pain for Middle-aged Workers." *The Paths to Productive Aging* (edited by M. Kumashiro). Bristol, Penn: Taylor and Francis, Ltd., 1995.

Ulrich, K.T., and S.D. Eppinger. *Product Design and Development.* New York: McGraw Hill, 1995.

Vora P.R., and M.G. Helander. "A Review of the Design Models and a Proposal for a Taxonomy of Design." *Design for Manufacturability* (edited by M. Helander and M. Nagamachi). Bristol, Penn: Taylor and Francis, Ltd., 1992.

Wall, B., R. Solum, and M. Sobol. *The Visionary Leader.* Rocklin, CA: Prima Publishing, 1992.

Weimer, J. *Research Techniques in Human Engineering.* Englewood Cliffs, N.J.: Prentice-Hall, 1995.

Wheatley, M. J. *Leadership and the New Science.* San Francisco: Berrett-Koehler Publishers, 1994.

White and Punjabi. *Biomechanics of the Spine.* Philadelphia, Pennsylvania: J.B. Lippincott Publishers, 1989.

Wilson, J. and E. Corlett (editors), second edition. *Evaluation of Human Work.* London: Taylor and Francis, 1995.

Winkel, Jorgen, and Rolfh Westgaard. "A Model for Solving Work-related Musculoskeletal Problems in a Profitable Way." *Applied Ergonomics* 27, no. 2 (1996).

Yam, P. "Mind Meets Machine, Sort Of." *Scientific American* (November 1995): 32.

de Zwart, B.C.H., J.P.J. Broersen, M.H.W. Frings-Dresen, F.J.H. van Dijk, and T.F. Meijman. "Indications for Selection on Musculoskeletal Complaints Among Aging Workers." *The Paths to Productive Aging* (edited by M. Kumashiro). Bristol, Penn.: Taylor and Francis, 1995.

illustration acknowledgments

Table 1-1: From Masaaki Imai, *Kaizen* (New York: Random House, 1986).

Figure 1-2: Adapted from P.G. Smith and D.G. Reinertsen, *Developing Products in Half the Time* (New York: Van Nostrand Reinhold, 1995). Reprinted by permission of Preston G. Smith.

Table 2-2: From Keki R. Bhote, *World Class Quality*. Copyright (c) 1991 AMACOM, a division of American Management Association. All rights reserved. Excerpted by permission of American Management Association.

Figure 2-3: Adapted from M. Helander, *A Guide to the Ergonomics of Manufacturing* (Bristol, Penn: Taylor & Francis, 1995). Reprinted by permission of Taylor & Francis.

Figure 2-7: Adapted from E. Asmussen, "Growth in Muscular Strength and Power," in G.L. Rarick, ed., *Physical Activity, Human Growth, and Development* (New York: Academic Press, 1973).

Figure 2-8: From M. Pitman and L. Peterson, "Biomechanics of Skeletal Muscle," in M. Nordin and V.H. Frankel, eds., *Biomechanics of the Musculoskeletal System* (Philadelphia: Lea and Febiger, 1989—an imprint of Williams and Wilkins). Reprinted by permission of Williams and Wilkins.

Figure 2-9: From R.L. Lieber, *Skeletal Muscle Structure and Function* (Baltimore: Williams and Wilkins, 1992). Reprinted by permission of Williams and Wilkins.

Table 3-1: Adapted from R.L. McCarthy, T.J. Ayres, C.T. Wood, and J.N. Robinson, "Risk and Effectiveness Criteria for Using on Product Warnings," in *Ergonomics*, Vol. 38/11 (Taylor & Francis, 1995). Reprinted by permission of Taylor & Francis.

Figure 3-4: From H. Gruber, "Aspects of Scientific Theory: Aesthetics and Cognition," in John Brockman, ed., *Creativity* (New York: Simon & Schuster, 1993).

Figure 3-8: Adapted from P.R. Vora and M.G. Helander, "A Review of the Design Models and a Proposal for a Taxonomy of Design," in M.

Helander and N. Nagamichi, eds., *Design for Manufacturing: A System Approach to Concurrent Engineering and Ergonomics* (Bristol, Penn: Taylor & Francis, 1992). Reprinted by permission of Taylor & Francis.

Figure 3-9: Adapted from E.G. Grossmith, "Product Design Considerations for the Reduction of Ergonomically Related Manufacturing Costs," in M. Helander and N. Nagamichi, eds., *Design for Manufacturing: A System Approach to Concurrent Engineering and Ergonomics* (Bristol, Penn: Taylor & Francis, 1992). Reprinted by permission of Taylor & Francis.

Figure 3-10: Adapted from K.T. Ulrich and S.D. Eppinger, *Product Design and Development* (New York: McGraw-Hill, 1995). Reprinted by permission of the McGraw-Hill Companies.

Figure 3-11: Adapted from James G. Bralla, *Design for Excellence* (New York: McGraw-Hill, 1996). Reprinted by permission of the McGraw-Hill Companies.

Figure 4-1: Adapted from P.G. Smith and D.G. Reinertsen, *Developing Products in Half the Time* (New York: Van Nostrand Reinhold, 1995). Reprinted by permission of Preston G. Smith.

Figure 4-2: Adapted from G. M. Hoffman, *The Technology Payoff* (Burr Ridge, Ill: Irwin Professional Publishing, 1994). Reprinted by permission of Irwin Professional Publishing.

Figure 4-3: Adapted from E. Grandjean, *Fitting the Task to the Man* (New York: Taylor & Francis, 4th ed. 1995). Reprinted by permission of Taylor & Francis.

Figure 4-4: From I.A. Kapandji, *The Physiology of the Joints* Vol. 3 (New York: Churchill Livingstone, 1974). Reprinted by permission of I.A. Kapandji.

Figure 5-1: Adapted from D.H. Besterfield, C. Besterfield-Michna, and M. Besterfield-Sacre, *Total Quality Management* (Englewood Cliffs: Prentice-Hall, 1995). Reprinted by permission of Prentice-Hall, Inc.

Figure 5-3: Adapted from L. Cohen, *Quality Function Deployment* (New York: Addison-Wesley, 1995). Copyright (c) 1995 Addison-Wesley Publishing Company, Inc. Reprinted by permission of Addison-Wesley Longman Publishing Company, Inc.

Figure 6-1: Adapted from P. Mears, *Quality Improvement Tools and Techniques* (New York: McGraw-Hill, 1995). Reprinted by permission of the McGraw-Hill Companies.

Figure 6-2: Adapted from M.A. Dalfonso, *ISO 9000: Achieving Compliance and Certification* (New York: John Wiley and Sons, 1995). Copyright (c) 1995 John Wiley and Sons, Inc. Reprinted by permission of John Wiley and Sons, Inc.

Figure 6-3: Adapted from P. Mears, *Quality Improvement Tools and Techniques* (New York: McGraw-Hill, 1995). Reprinted by permission of the McGraw-Hill Companies.

Figure 7-1: Art created from data in Bureau of Labor Statistics (BLS), Department of Labor, *Work Injuries and Illnesses by Selected Characteristics,* 1981–1994.

Table 7-1: Adapted from I. Kuorinka and I. Forcier, *Work Related Musculoskeletal Disorders* (Bristol, Penn:Taylor & Francis, 1995). Reprinted by permission of Taylor & Francis.

Table 7-2: From Yair Lifshitz and Thomas J. Armstrong, "A Design Checklist for Control and Prediction of Cumulative Trauma Disorder in Intensive Manual Jobs," in *Proceedings of the Human Factors Society 30th Annual Meeting.* Copyright (c) 1986 by the Human Factors and Ergonomics Society. All rights reserved. Reprinted by permission of the Human Factors and Ergonomics Society.

Figure 7-3: Art created from data in Dan MacLeod, *The Ergonomics Edge: Improving Safety, Quality, and Productivity* (New York: Van Nostrand Reinhold, 1995).

Figure 7-4: Art created from data in Dan MacLeod, *The Ergonomics Edge: Improving Safety, Quality, and Productivity* (New York: Van Nostrand Reinhold, 1995).

Figure 7-5: From Dan MacLeod, *Ergonomics Success in the Meat Industry* (New Jersey: Clayton Environmental Consultants, 1996). Reprinted by permission of Dan McLeod.

Figure 7-6: From I.A. Kapandji, *The Physiology of the Joints* Vol. 3 (New York: Churchill Livingstone, 1974). Reprinted by permission of I.A. Kapandji.

Figure 7-7: From I.A. Kapandji, *The Physiology of the Joints* Vol. 3 (New York: Churchill Livingstone, 1974). Reprinted by permission of I.A. Kapandji.

Figure 7-8: From White and Punjabi, *Biomechanics of the Spine* (Philadelphia: J.B. Lippincott Publishers, 1989). Reprinted by permission of Lippincott-Raven Publishers.

Figure 7-9: From D.B. Chaffin and K.S. Parks, "A Longitudinal Study of Low Back Pain as Associated with Occupational Lifting Factors," in *American Industrial Hygiene Association Journal* 34, 1973. Reprinted by permission of the American Industrial Hygiene Association.

Figure 7-10: Adapted from E. Grandjean, *Fitting the Task to the Man* (New York: Taylor & Francis, 4th ed. 1995). Reprinted by permission of Taylor & Francis.

Figure 7-11: From E. Grandjean, *Fitting the Task to the Man* (New York: Taylor & Francis, 4th ed. 1995). Reprinted by permission of Taylor & Francis.

Figure 7-12: Adapted from V. Putz-Anderson, *Cumulative Trauma Disorders* (Bristol, Penn: Taylor & Francis, 1994). Reprinted by permission of Taylor & Francis.

Figure 7-13: From V. Putz-Anderson, *Cumulative Trauma Disorders* (Bristol, Penn: Taylor & Francis, 1994). Reprinted by permission of Taylor & Francis.

Figure 7-14: From I.A. Kapandji, *The Physiology of the Joints* Vol. 3 (NewYork: Churchill Livingstone, 1974). Reprinted by permission of I.A. Kapandji.

Figure 7-16: Adapted from M. Helander, *A Guide to the Ergonomics of Manufacturing* (Bristol, Penn: Taylor & Francis, 1995). Reprinted by permission of Taylor & Francis.

Figure 7-17: From T.D. Schneid, *The Americans with Disabilities Act* (New York: Van Nostrand Reinhold, 1992). Reprinted by permission of Van Nostrand Reinhold.

Figure 7-18: Adapted from BCAM International, Inc., "Flow Chart of the Ergonomic Data Acquisition Process." Reprinted by permission of BCAM International, Inc.

Figure 8-1: Art created from data reported in H. McRae, "The World in 2020," from *The Harvard Business School Press*, 1994.

Figure 8-2: Adapted from B. Wall, R. Solum, and M. Sobol, *The Visionary Leader* (Rocklin, Calif: Prima Publishing, 1992). Reprinted by permission of Prima Publishing.

Figure 8-4: Adapted from P. Mears. *Quality Improvement Tools and Techniques* (New York: McGraw-Hill, 1995). Reprinted by permission of the McGraw-Hill Companies.

Figure 8-6: Adapted from Daniel Stamp, *The Invisible Assembly Line.* Copyright (c) 1995 Daniel Stamp. Published by AMACOM, a division of American Management Association. All rights reserved. Excerpted by permission of the publisher.

Figure 8-7: Adapted from Families and Work Institute, "The Changing Workforce," in P. Bernstein and C. Ma, eds., *The Practical Guide to Practically Everything* (New York: McGraw-Hill, 1995).

Figure 9-1: Adapted from James G. Bralla, *Design for Excellence* (New York: McGraw-Hill, 1996). Reprinted by permission of the McGraw-Hill Companies.

Figure 9-2: Adapted from K.T. Ulrich and S.D. Eppinger, *Product Design and Development* (New York: McGraw-Hill, 1995). Reprinted by permission of the McGraw-Hill Companies.

Figure 9-3: Adapted from J.D. Hunger and T.L. Wheelen, *Strategic Management* (Reading, Mass: Addison-Wesley, 1996) . Copyright (c) 1996 Addison-Wesley Publishing Company, Inc. Reprinted by permission of Addison-Wesley Longman Publishing Company, Inc.

Figure 9-4: From E. Miller, A. Loughlin, E. Nudelman, and D. Thomas (editors of "Research Alert") in *Future Vision* (Naperville, Ill: Sourcebooks Trade, 1991). Reprinted by permission of Sourcebooks Trade.

Pages 179 to 182, Option Generator: From D.J. Noone, *Creative Problem Solving* (Hauppauge, New York: Barron's Educational Services, 1993). Reprinted by permission of Barron's Educational Services.

about the author

Dr. Clifford M. Gross is a leader in the emerging field of biomechanically based ergonomics. He received his masters and Ph.D. degrees from New York University. He was the Acting Director of the Graduate Program in Ergonomics and Biomechanics at NYU and Chairman of the Department of Biomechanics at The New York Institute of Technology. Dr. Gross founded The Biomechanics Corporation of America.

While at this biomechanics technology company, Dr. Gross served as the Chief Executive Officer and Chairman of the Board for eleven years and established corporate ergonomic quality programs for many Fortune 500 companies. He is currently a Research Professor at the University of South Florida, College of Public Health as well as the Director of the university's Center for Product Ergonomics. Dr. Gross is a Certified Professional Ergonomist (CPE) and a Fellow of the Ergonomics Society.

index

books from productivity press

Productivity Press publishes books that empower individuals and companies to achieve excellence in quality, productivity, and the creative involvement of all employees. Through steadfast efforts to support the vision and strategy of continuous improvement, Productivity Press delivers today's leading-edge tools and techniques gathered directly from industrial leaders around the world. *Call toll-free 1-800-394-6868 for our free catalog.*

STEPPING UP TO ISO 14000
Integrating Environmental Quality with ISO 9000 and TQM
Subash C. Puri

The newest ISO standards, announced in mid-1996, require environmentally-friendly practices in every aspect of a manufacturing business, from factory design and raw material acquisition to the production, packaging, distribution, and ultimate disposal of the product. Here's a comprehensible overview and implementation guide to the standards that's also the only one to show how they fit with current ISO 9000 efforts and other companywide programs for Total Quality Management (TQM).
ISBN 1-56327-129-X / 280 pages / $39.00 / Order STPISO-B272

THE HUNTERS AND THE HUNTED
A Non-Linear Solution for Reengineering the Workplace
James B. Swartz

Our competitive environment changes rapidly. If you want to survive, you have to stay on top of those changes. Hunters continuously change and learn; anyone who doesn't becomes the hunted and sooner or later will be devoured. This unusual non-fiction novel provides a veritable crash course in continuous transformation. Lessons from real-life companies. *The Hunters and the Hunted* puts you inside the change process itself.
ISBN 1-56327-043-9 / 582 pages / $45.00 / Order HUNT-B272

LEARNING ORGANIZATIONS
Developing Cultures for Tomorrow's Workplace
Sarita Chawla and John Renesch, Editors

The ability to learn faster than your competition may be your only sustainable competitive advantage! A learning organization is one where people continually expand their capacity to create results they truly desire, where new and expansive patterns of thinking are nurtured, where collective aspiration is set free, and where people are continually learning how to learn together. This compilation of 34 powerful essays, written by recognized experts worldwide, is rich in concept and theory as well as application and example. An inspiring followup to Peter Senge's groundbreaking bestseller *The Fifth Discipline*.
ISBN 1-56327-110-9 / 575 pages / $35.00 / Order LEARN-B272

PRODUCT DESIGN REVIEW
A Methodology for Error-Free Product Development
Compiled by Takashi Ichida; edited by Edward C. Voigt

Design Review is a powerful new method for quality assurance in product design. A systematic 7-step way to manage the design process, it ensures the highest quality products at the lowest cost and in the shortest time frame. Six case studies show how easy it is to customize this flexible method. A practical book for managers and design engineers in all manufacturing environments.
ISBN 1-56327-041-2 / 360 pages / $85.00 / Order PDR-B272

IMPLEMENTING A LEAN MANAGEMENT SYSTEM
Thomas L. Jackson with Karen R. Jones

Does your company think and act ahead of technological change, ahead of the customer, and ahead of the competition? Thinking strategically requires a company to face these questions with a clear future image of itself. *Implementing a Lean Management System* lays out a comprehensive management system for aligning the firm's vision of the future with market realities. Based on the Japanese strategic planning method used by top managers for driving TQM, Lean Management is about deploying vision, strategy, and policy to all levels of daily activity. Key tools build on the knowledge worker, multiskilling, and understanding the role and responsibilities of the new lean manufacturer.
ISBN 1-56327-085-4 / 182 pages / $65.00 / Order ILMS-B272

Order By E-mail: Order 24 hours a day from anywhere in the world.
Use either address:
To order: service@ppress.com
To view the online catalog and/or order: http://www.ppress.com

Note: *Prices are in U.S. dollars and are subject to change without notice.*